# Having
# Cancer

# Having Cancer

&

## HOW TO LIVE WITH IT

# Angela Wilkie

Hodder & Stoughton
LONDON SYDNEY AUCKLAND

British Library Cataloguing in Publication Data

Wilkie, Angela
  Having Cancer: How to Live with it
  I. Title
  362.1

  ISBN 0-340-58516-1

First published in Great Britain 1993

Published by Hodder and Stoughton,
a division of Hodder and Stoughton Ltd,
Mill Road, Dunton Green, Sevenoaks, Kent TN13 2YA.
Editorial Office: 47 Bedford Square, London WC1B 3DP.

Photoset by Rowland Phototypesetting Ltd,
Bury St Edmunds, Suffolk

Printed in Great Britain by
Clays Ltd, St Ives plc

# Acknowledgements

First, my thanks to all the countless family and friends who helped us in so many ways.

Thanks to all who wrote or spoke to me about their own cancer experience, particularly Shirley Murray, who must have got sick of hearing, 'I just wanted to ask you something about . . .'!

Thanks to Val Speechley, head of Patient Education at the Royal Marsden Hospital, who kindly gave her time to read the medical information contained in the book.

Thanks to Celia Levett, who believed in the book and gave endless encouragement.

And above all, many thanks to Berry Ritchie, who took an idea and made it happen.


The author and publishers would like to thank the following for their kind permission to reproduce the quotations contained in this book:

Clare McIntyre for the quotation from her play, *My Heart's A Suitcase*

Faber & Faber Ltd for the quotation from 'Hic Et Ille' from W H Auden's *The Dyer's Hand*

A P Watt Ltd on behalf of The Trustees of The Robert Graves' Copyright Trust, for the quotation from Robert Graves' *The Greek Myths*

Hodder & Stoughton Ltd for the quotation from John le Carré's *The Secret Pilgrim*

William Heinemann Ltd for the quotation from Penelope Lively's *Perfect Happiness*

Bloomsbury Publishing for the quotation from Margaret
  Attwood's *Cat's Eye*
Flamingo, an imprint of HarperCollinsPublishers Ltd, for
  the quotation from Amy Tan's *The Kitchen God's Wife*
Warner Chappell Music for the quotation from the lyrics of
  Joni Mitchell's 'Trouble Child'

# Contents

Author's Note    ix
Introduction    xi

*Part One: Having Cancer*

1  Banging My Head Against A Brick Wall    5
2  Precious Poisons    18
3  'It's Back'    22
4  A Glimpse Over The Edge    34
5  The Road Back    48
6  My Very Own *Star Wars*    54
7  Learning To Live With Cancer    60
8  In Remission, Or The First Five Years Are
     The Worst    68

*Part Two: How to Live With It*

9  How Not To Be Brave    77
10  Your Family And Other Liabilities    89
11  Relaxation, Focusing And Negative Thinking    99
12  In The Hands Of The Experts    104
13  Going Into Hospital: Before, During And After    112
14  Investigations, Treatment, Drugs And Medical
     Paraphernalia    118
15  Getting Help    132
16  Back To The Future    137

# Author's Note

Anyone who has to fight their way through the experience of cancer deserves a government grant (or the vast royalties of a hugely successful self-help book) to fund their yacht, their Mercedes sports car, or whatever fantasy they hold most dear. Personally, I'd love a season ticket to the house in France that brought me such peace in some of my darkest times. But because there are more of us every day, and because there's never enough money, every penny I earn from this book will have to go to the Royal Marsden Hospital, because they saved my life and thousands of others, and to Cancer Research, so that there will be a time when people like us don't have to live in terror any more.

# Introduction

*I'll tell you what this isn't. It isn't a story of how I bravely battled against cancer and lived to find true happiness. It isn't about how facing death made me a better and wiser person. It's about how I've been living with cancer and felt angry, despairing and isolated. And how I think we – and there are a lot of us about – have every right to feel that way.*

This is the opening paragraph of the article I wrote that was published in *Woman* on 20 January 1992. The heading read: *Angela Wilkie is our letters page editor. She also suffers from cancer. We thought the article she's written here was so powerful because we know her. Then we realised it's because it expresses what so few victims admit to – anger!*

In this article, I said that I was fed up with being told how cancer would lead to a fuller understanding of life, or my spiritual growth, or even that it could provide my first true freedom in life – all theories I'd read shortly before I threw the books across the room screaming. Frankly, I was too concerned as to whether my husband and children would very soon have to manage without me to spend a great deal of time appreciating how far my consciousness was being raised.

The article was followed by a flood of telephone calls and letters which are still coming in. Without exception, they express the same sentiments. To quote but four:

*It was harrowing to read, but it is one of the most constructive articles I have ever read on the subject.*

*How refreshing to read how angry you are . . .*

*I went through exactly the same emotions . . .*

*Only a person suffering from cancer could write that article; only a person with cancer could know how it feels . . .*

Alongside the article, I offered some brief advice for fellow sufferers to help them cope with cancer. These tips told readers that they couldn't afford to take on anybody else's emotional baggage; that tiredness is the great enemy; not to bottle up their feelings; to cry when they need to, but not to panic; to concentrate on one goal at a time; not to be too hard on themselves and, most important of all, to tell themselves again and again, 'I can get through this!'

I finally made up my mind to write this book because of an encounter at the Royal Marsden Hospital about a year ago. I'd just had my regular check-up, and I was feeling great because I'd just been told I could switch to six-monthly appointments. Another step forward, and it was a wonderful boost. I went along to collect my drugs with a big grin on my face, almost bouncing with relief and optimism. In the waiting area were a woman and her husband, and she had an expression I recognised only too well. It was the stricken, bewildered face of someone who's just starting out on treatment, and who's trying to absorb the knowledge that her life has just had a big hole punched in it.

I wanted so badly to help, to say something, anything, that might give her a bit of comfort or let her know that the task ahead wasn't as impossible as it looked. But we don't, do we, we British? We're worried about intruding or interfering or saying the wrong thing. So I just smiled weakly and went off with my pills, but I thought about her all night and how hard, how intolerably hard it is to walk this road.

When I knew for certain that I had cancer, I wanted to know how it would feel, how other people had coped with the experience. But I had to learn the hard way, because nothing I was told or read prepared me for what actually happened to me or how I felt before, during and after my treatment. The advice I found in books and articles seemed to be written by doctors and psychologists (who had experience of the treatment, but not the disease), or by patients who seem to have sailed through cancer and its treatment by sheer strength of character. This didn't happen to me. I read a lot about spiritual growth and how I could discover new insights into life and its meaning. This didn't happen to me. I read that I could end up a deeper and better person – this certainly didn't happen to me.

At first I felt weak and inadequate when faced with all this material trailing clouds of glory. These people said I could cope with panic and exhaustion, so why couldn't I? These people didn't lie awake night after night, too shocked even to cry, so I must be lacking in moral fibre. Everything I had read boiled down to Thinking Positive – but I couldn't.

Then, very slowly, I started to feel not weak, but angry. How dare these people suggest that what was tearing my life apart was some glorious challenge that would bring out the best in me? How dare they take an ugly and cruel disease like cancer and apply rules to it, as if patients could follow steps one to ten and everything would be fine? And most of all, why should they make me feel ashamed because I couldn't grin and bear it?

Of course we always want to make sense of our experiences, to find a meaning or something positive in our most difficult times. But that can come only in retrospect, which is why I found no comfort in being told where all this was leading me, instead of being given help with the overwhelming experience of serious illness and its impact on my life.

It reminded me very much of all the advice and literature I'd seen before I had my first baby. At that time the emphasis was on 'natural childbirth': the idea was implicit that if one opted for pain-relieving drugs or ended up with stitches, one had somehow failed to live up to the true ideal of womanhood. Breast-feeding got the same treatment. One must strive to overcome any difficulties or discomfort because only breast was really good enough. I failed dismally on both counts. The birth was painful and difficult; my son was a big baby who was never satisfied with what I could provide. We were both miserable for months, simply because I was desperate to live up to what 'the books' told me was the right way to perform. Just as I now realise that those ideas, absorbed from those who were supposed to know all about it, were only a small part of the truth, I believe that popular doctrine about cancer has distorted the truth to fit the theories. And I still feel that the cult of positive thinking has taken a grain of truth, a smidgen of common sense and created a whole mythology out of it.

So this is the book I needed to read when I started out on two years of cancer treatment. It is not technical, although it does describe what happens to cancer patients at the hands of doctors and nurses. Medical knowledge and detail is, in the context of cancer, secondary to how it feels to be on the receiving end of the disease and its treatment. It will not waffle about personal growth or spiritual insights. It is simply an unvarnished description of what it is *really* like to have cancer. How it feels to discover you have a potentially life-threatening disease. How it feels to hand yourself over to a range of treatments that sound barbaric. And how it feels to reach levels of fear and despair people should never have to encounter the whole of their lives.

I don't want to frighten people more than they are already frightened. I don't want to paint a picture of doom and gloom, because that's not accurate either. I want to tell the truth as I found it, because I believe that the unknown is worse than being prepared and the truth can even allay fear. I certainly found many of the actual treatments less gruesome than I had been led to believe. I want to suggest ways of coping with some of the endless obstacles you'll meet, and to help you concentrate on your triumphs as each skirmish is fought and won.

You are starting a long hard slog, but you will get through it one way or another. Not because it will show how much guts you've got, though it will. Not because it will bring self-revelation, though it might. You are going to get through it because you simply have no choice, other than to lie down and die. However bad things get, keep hold of this thought: more and more of us are coming out the other side of this nightmare. We are in remission, or we are clear of disease after one, two, ten or twenty years. Or we are at a stage that can be brought under long-term control by drugs.

There *is* Life After Cancer. There is life during cancer, for that matter, and not all the days will be tough ones. You *can* be happy and peaceful again.

To every cancer sufferer reading this book, I wish you the best of luck, and I hope you find something here to help you.

# PART ONE

---

*Having Cancer*

Part One of this book deals with my personal experience of cancer. I have tried to be as honest as I could, so that hopefully others can be better prepared than I was. If some of the incidents seem frightening, remember that I did recover from them. If it seems that there was a lot of pressure and misery, remember that these events took place over more than two years: there were lots of calm times as well. Remember also that many patients will never develop secondary disease.

Part Two offers some practical suggestions to help what can be helped. Some of the ideas may seem tough or hard-hearted, I know, but I strongly believe that as cancer patients, we simply cannot afford distractions when we are fighting for our lives. There will be time to be nice unselfish people again when we're well.

The quotes I've used at the start of some chapters are thoughts that helped me at various times. I found them in books or newspapers, on the radio or in conversation. The only thing they have in common is that none of them originally had anything whatever to do with cancer!

Recently I discovered what the words of my favourite Italian aria meant in English. I'd loved it for years, with only a vague idea of its meaning. How odd and appropriate to discover that the translation of the last line is, 'I have never loved life so much.' I hope you find the same when your bad times are behind you.

# 1

# Banging My Head
# Against A Brick Wall

*I did not want to be coddled by casseroles. Kindness was compensation. Kindness was a reminder that my life had changed, was always changing, that people thought I should just accept all this and become strong or brave, more enlightened, more peaceful. I wanted nothing to do with that. I wanted to live my life with the same focus as other people.*

Amy Tan, THE KITCHEN GOD'S WIFE

I can remember so clearly standing at the window of a friend's house in May 1990. It was a sunny spring day and the garden was full of colour. I'd come from yet another doctor's appointment to collect my children, walking back into my normal life as if nothing was wrong. But for months I had been in growing pain, and was so tired all the time. I'd gone several times to my NHS group practice, but the answer was always the same. No big deal; it's constipation, it's stress, it's fine. I had even started to believe that it must all be in my head, but thank God I was bolshy and self-opinionated enough to keep on seeking other opinions. I knew my body, I told myself; I knew there was something to explain this pain and exhaustion. But still the same answer came back: it was anxiety. So I stood at the window on that May afternoon and thought, in total desolation and absolute conviction: *I've got cancer, and no one will listen to me.*

I'd voiced that fear to a doctor a few months before, but

because of the location of the pain, all investigation was centred on my bowel. When the results were negative, I am certain that they felt this clinched the matter. I was a young woman, working at home part-time with two children. They couldn't find anything, so I was neurotic. QED.

I'd been steadily losing weight. At first I was delighted, and thought my new exercise class must be working really well. Now I was terrified. Going to the loo was difficult and painful. I took pain-killers every four hours for weeks. Still I was told I was well. My husband was worried, and supported my feeling that I had to go on looking for answers, but no doubt my irritability and growing lethargy were hard to endure.

We went on an Easter holiday which was a complete disaster; the pain and lack of energy combined with my extreme susceptibility to cold made each day a trial rather than a pleasure. Luckily we were staying on a farm so at least the children could play with calves and piglets and puppies, but the strain on our marriage was enormous. And because I'd been told so often that there was nothing wrong with me, I'm sure there were times when my husband couldn't help wondering if there really were mental problems behind my behaviour.

All the other holiday homes were full of happy families going on brisk walks and playing on the beaches. I felt completely cut off from them, wanting only to lie down whenever I could. But when I did lie down alone, my mind was in turmoil. Was I really having some kind of break-down? Was the pain indeed all in my mind? Perhaps I secretly wanted to go back to work, but was too afraid to admit it. Perhaps in some corner of my mind I was dissatisfied with my life, or my family. My faith that doctors knew best was in constant conflict with my certainty that I knew my own body, and that I had to be seriously ill.

When we came home and I discovered that I'd lost still more weight, I decided to get a second (or sixth or seventh) opinion. I went to a Well Woman clinic, told my story – and once more was examined and pronounced fine. There was no medical reason for my pain. I asked to be sent for ovarian screening, because I'd heard from friends that ovarian cysts can be hard to diagnose, and the symptoms sounded somewhat similar. I was told it wasn't necessary. I insisted. I went to be screened, and was told that the operator couldn't discern my ovaries on ultrasound. This, I was then told, was a good sign, as when they're normal they're quite small and hard to spot. So as she couldn't spot them, they were probably normal. A snip at £125! I wasn't satisfied, and asked to be screened again. It was quite clear by now that my reputation as a hopeless neurotic was well established, but they agreed reluctantly to another appointment.

This time it took a consultant radiologist about thirty seconds to tell me, 'If you were my wife, I'd want this looked at straightaway.' Those words, and my own bolshiness, probably saved my life.

Strangely enough, there was no panic, or even anger at that moment. What I felt was almost elation that at last somebody had taken me seriously. I had been right all along, but it had taken fifteen months to prove it. I kept laughing, probably in shock, at the old joke about the inscription on the hypochondriac's gravestone, 'I told you I was ill!'

After that, things happened very fast. A blood test, which revealed my haemoglobin level was dangerously low. An examination by a consultant gynaecologist, who wanted me in hospital three days later. I'd wasted all that time trying to get somebody to listen, and now the pace was too fast. I needed time to control my rising panic. The word cancer was never used, but I knew that there wouldn't be all this rush if they weren't pretty sure it was serious. And somehow, I never came out and said, 'Do you think it's cancer?', as if somehow that would be bad manners, that I shouldn't be the one to utter the dreaded word. As if saying it would make it true.

I actually waited a week before going into hospital, feeling I needed time to prepare the children and make arrangements for them; time for my husband and me to tie up things at work. I wish now I hadn't waited. The days seemed endless; my elation became mixed with rising panic. Some of the time I would feel as if I were watching myself go through the motions of my everyday life, in a sort of dream-like slowed-down reality. Sometimes I'd get hyped up and make morbid jokes to relieve the tension, talking too fast about how it was a routine operation these days, wasn't it, and how the surgeon who was doing it had such a great reputation (he has), and how it was all going to be fine.

I hated telling my boss, my children's teachers, and all the daily social network what was about to happen. I cringed from the look in their eyes, the awkward sympathy, because I felt that if once I broke down, I might never be able to stop. I tried to keep the week as normal as possible, making plans for friends to help with the children.

The biggest strain was feeling I had to put on a good show for our families and friends. Some of those who were closest to us seemed unable to deal with the situation and were very distressing to be with. Their reactions made us feel that somehow we had no right to burden them with the depth of what faced us, that we were responsible for keeping up their spirits. I felt I was required to spare them as much as possible, to talk briskly and positively and be the person they'd always known. But again anger came to my rescue. I started to resent the way they clearly expected the worst from the beginning, and were centring their reactions on their own fear and anxiety. It made me feel let down and very isolated, but worse, it was very draining. Trying to be strong for anyone else's sake but that of our two children was too big a strain on our dwindling energies. It was an expression of their love for us, but a demanding not a supporting one. By the time the day of the operation arrived, we were definitely working on the principle: If you can't stand the heat, stay out of the kitchen.

The last time I was alone in the house before the operation, I felt I had to write some letters to my husband and our children, in case anything went wrong. This was the hardest thing I've ever done. I started to cry again and again, but when they were written, it brought me some kind of peace, as if I'd prepared myself as far as I could.

We kept the weekend before my operation as normal as possible. We took the children to the pub and my husband and I even went out for a meal. I suppose it was a sort of defiance, as if we were simply refusing to be rolled over by what was happening. All these memories run in my head like a video; I can remember exactly what we said, what we wore, and how it felt. We were really quite relaxed, ready to do what we had to, although a last-minute hitch in the arrangements for the children added to the strain. We didn't even talk much about it, neither of us wanting to add to the other's burden, but we were probably as close then as at the births of our children. It was very comforting, and it gave me a lot of strength.

I had told the children in basic terms, and in my best matter-of-fact voice, what was going to happen. It was a blessed relief that they were too young (five and three) to be aware of the implications, so they accepted it without too much upset, although in the few days before I went into hospital, they often asked the same questions again and again. I think this was as much to do with their realisation of the tension in us as with any worry of their own. They knew all the people who were to be helping with them, and although I was unhappy that they would be out of their normal routine, they took it all as a big adventure. I was proud that they were secure enough not to be thrown at the idea of my being away for the first time in their lives.

My husband's firm was marvellous in helping with time off and altered hours, and a good friend of mine, who often looked after my daughter when I was working, was to be in charge of both children when my husband was at the hospital. Knowing that the practical details were so well taken care of relieved a lot of unnecessary extra pressure.

The morning of the operation was full of domestic detail, and I was able to absorb myself in lost socks and lunch money. We were due at the hospital at 9 a.m. and I was pleased that we wouldn't have to hang around at home. Some hope. We arrived on time, the administration details were dealt with – and we waited. For hour after morale-sapping hour, with nothing to do but try to control our thoughts of what lay ahead and how much depended on it. We soon realised that everyone on the day's operating list had been required to arrive at the same time, and that we had to fill half a day within the bounds of the hospital. We tried to talk about anything but the operation; we tried to read or watch TV; we went for silly little walks because we'd been admitted, hadn't we, so we couldn't leave the hospital premises. I couldn't have any pills either, because of the coming anaesthetic, so my pain was very severe. It was like a refined form of torture, and I was never given any other explanation than that it suited the surgeons.

By the time the pre-med injection arrived, we'd been there for seven hours. But once it began to take effect everything was fine, and I was able to drift happily through the rest of the waiting time. My husband had to manage without the benefit of narcotics, but at least they did give him a cup of coffee every so often. By the time the porters arrived to take me down to the operating theatre, I was calm, a bit vague, but quite untroubled. I am very fond of pre-meds.

On the way down to theatre, I felt as if I was in one of those awful made-for-TV movies which always start with a view of ceilings and tops of doors, as the camera pretends to be the patient on the trolley. The theatre staff all made little jokes, but still told me exactly what they were about to do which was very reassuring; then a little jab and good night, Vienna.

I came round in the recovery room just long enough for the staff to reassure themselves that all was well, then zonked out for another few hours. Once again my husband bore the worst of it, as I moaned about the pain and how much it hurt, which was terrible for him, and of which I have absolutely no recollection whatsoever. The consultant was due to see us after the operation, which thought must have stuck in my mind because much, much later I asked the nurse if he'd arrived yet. I was told he'd seen my husband hours before and both of them had long gone home. All I was aware of was the mild sting of another needle in my bottom and off I went again.

I was given regular pain-relieving injections all that night and some of the following day. When I was rather more awake, the nurses got me up to start walking around (with their support) which is important after surgery, but still I was in no pain. I had a catheter to drain out urine, a drain from the operation site and a drip in my arm. Occasionally in the days that followed, the catheter would drag and that was uncomfortable, or I'd accidentally pull the drip and that would sting, but I was never in any real pain after that operation, and I'm a real wimp about pain. I hope this can help reassure anyone who's worried about that aspect of surgery, as I was. I didn't even need to ask for the drugs; they had already been written up by the surgeon.

When I was really fully conscious again, I started to feel marvellous. The operation was over; I felt good, I was in no pain – and I'd made it! I had lots of visitors, I walked round the hospital (complete with drip and drain), I had lots of sleep and ate like a horse. After three days we decided I was presentable enough to see the children, so we carefully hid all the attached bottles under the bedclothes and I sat up, so excited to see them again. It was lovely; they were bouncy and full of questions. It took the three-year-old about two minutes to find the drain bottle, half full of blood, which she shook around gleefully crying, 'What's this, Mummy?' Her more sensitive and less ghoulish older brother was a bit upset by this, but was soon reassured by the fact that I was obviously not suffering. In fact, I looked better than I had for months; all the blood I'd been given meant I had pink fingertips rather than grey ones. I was reassured that the kids were fine and happy, so the only person who was really suffering was my poor husband, rushing between the kids and the hospital and trying to go to work for the odd day in between. And of course nobody was taking any notice of him, when in fact he was the one under the most pressure.

After several days, we were told that the tumours that had been removed during the radical hysterectomy were definitely cancerous. This crushed the faint hope that the growths could be benign, and all I could do was stare at the surgeon who'd performed the operation, as if to get some clue of how I was supposed to react. He held my hand, in best bedside manner, and I wondered vaguely how on earth these poor doctors ever get used to telling people that their worst fears are now reality. He was very kind, and told us that he was asking an oncologist to see us to explain what would happen next. He also told us that the tissue samples taken from other organs during the hysterectomy appeared to be clear of disease. This seemed like good news, but then he began to say things like, '. . . if you're alive after five years . . .', which was information I was in no real condition to deal with. All we could manage at that moment was to absorb just the word cancer.

So he went, leaving us to smile at each other as well as we could and just hold onto each other. I don't remember that we said very much, but neither do I remember that I felt particularly panic-stricken. I suppose I was still so zonked from all the drugs that I was safeguarded from the full weight of what we had been told. I still felt very much as though we could handle whatever was coming, and I've since been told by other friends who've gone through hysterectomies that they too experienced this rush of euphoria – another thing to put down to my hormones!

That night happened to be the date of the World Cup concert in Rome when José Carreras, Placido Domingo and Luciano Pavarotti sang for the world. It was a wonderful occasion, but how much more special for anyone facing mountainous odds. To see Carreras, who so comparatively recently had been given less than a ten per cent chance of survival in his fight against leukaemia, perform a demanding repertoire, was the most enormous support and encouragement for me on that day when I'd been told the worst news I'd ever heard. The musical hero of my college days, the world's greatest romantic tenor, was back in his element to show us all that there was always hope when the human spirit simply refused to give in. His face showed the strain of what he'd endured; he had lost his curly dark locks, but he had come through hell and back to be a star again.

And when the concert included a song which I remembered my father, who had been dead for twenty years, singing to me as a child – 'You Are My Heart's Delight' from *Land of Smiles*, I cried for the first time since the surgeon had told us the news that afternoon. I'd never known the song was an operatic aria (my Dad was always singing all sorts of odds and ends), and I really felt as if the whole thing had been orchestrated simply to propel me forward with tremendous new energy and optimism. I felt as if the spirit of my father was behind me, that he would help me beat the same disease that had beaten him all those years ago. I'd missed him so much, especially since the grandchildren he'd never known had come along. He'd always kept a childlike quality that would have made him the most wonderful grandad.

This probably sounds ridiculously schmaltzy, but that's how it felt. It meant a great deal to me – one of those moments that could never be forgotten, when everything before you seems clear and promising. The only thing that stopped it being pure Hollywood was the fact that it wasn't Carreras who sang the song I remembered. I don't remember who won the World Cup that year, but I'll remember that night for the rest of my life.

The next day two friends came to visit bringing a bottle of champagne and some chocolate truffles. We sat outside in the sunshine, and as we talked and laughed I knew that I had made another new start. I felt that I was in charge of myself again and ready to face the next problem. That evening, the oncologist came to see us. She was marvellous, reassuring and optimistic that the course of treatment she was proposing would deal with any risk that disease remained, even though the pathology reports had all been negative. She even described my type of cancer as 'very ordinary, middle of the road' which was so dismissive it seemed she could deal with it without breaking sweat. Chemotherapy was to be a kind of insurance policy, just to make sure. She explained the whole process and all its possible bad aspects, such as sickness and the impact of the treatment on the blood. She also wanted to have a body scan done, to see the best possible picture of my insides, also explaining what that would involve. All our questions were answered with an air of quiet confidence that gave a great boost to our spirits.

Over the next couple of days, the catheter, drip and drain were gradually taken away one by one, leaving me feeling almost weightless as I did my therapeutic march up and down the corridors. My first bath was just wonderful, and a friend helped me to wash my hair, which by this time was a real social service. I felt so good compared with all the doom and gloom I'd read and heard about. It was easy to look on the brightest possible side, although I obviously tired easily and wasn't allowed any exertion. I was reminded of what I was *not* supposed to do when I unthinkingly started to drag an armchair across for a visitor and got screamed at by a nurse who wanted to know what the hell I was doing. She was very nice, but very graphic about what risks I was running by trying to do too much too soon, no matter how well I felt.

After just over a week I was able to go home, which was lovely. But away from the care of the nurses and the constant bed rest of the hospital, I think it's almost inevitable that you lose a little bit of ground. I was so happy to be back, but tired more quickly then I had in hospital, I suppose because there was more I wanted to do. I went down in the car with my husband to collect my son from Boys Brigade to give him a surprise, but although the look on his face was one I wouldn't have missed for anything, I found that the jolting of the car made me very uncomfortable, and I couldn't even close the heavy car door without help. I also felt rather vulnerable out in the open air: a bit unsteady as if I might fall over or lose my balance.

The first night in my own bed was marvellous. To me it was the most comfortable thing in the world after the hard, sweaty hospital mattress. Having silence and darkness after the ward's constant hum of activity with lights that were only dimmed at night seemed the height of luxury. It was great to be with the children again (I'd never been away from them before for more than a night) and for a few days my son kept checking I was still there which showed me how hard it had been on him. But we soon got back to normal. This was such a pleasant time for me – sleeping a lot, sitting in the sun and eating nice meals and mountains of chocolates! I was weak, but quite without pain for the first time in months and still very much on a high at having passed the first hurdle. I pottered round the garden, read even more books and magazines, had lots of visitors and lots of help. It was still hard to remember not to lift anything and to be careful of my stomach muscles. My scar was so neat and unobtrusive that it was difficult to comprehend what had been done and how much time the muscles would need to heal.

After nearly two weeks of this delightful holiday, I felt a pain in my shoulder, as if I'd pulled a muscle. The sensation was of pins and needles, but certainly not excruciating. Because of my recent operation, we decided we'd better call the doctor. The GP who arrived turned out to be one who had assured me six months before that my only problem was constipation, so when she said it was a chest infection perhaps we should have been more sceptical. Nevertheless, for several days I obediently took the antibiotics she prescribed. There was no improvement, so we asked for another visit.

This time another doctor decided I should go for an X-ray, as she thought there was a chance it could be an embolism (blood clot following surgery). I couldn't believe there was anything wrong as I felt so good, but when I turned up at the hospital for the X-ray I was re-admitted. There were several more tests which showed that I had emboli in both lungs, and I was immediately put on anti-coagulant drugs to thin out my blood and hopefully disperse the clots.

I went into a major sulk about this, worrying about the effect my second disappearance would have on the children, and feeling very fed up that yet again I was tied to a machine and a drip just days after I'd got rid of the first lot. I was very grumpy and ungracious and kept asking how long it would take, saying I felt fine until the doctor in charge finally got exasperated and told me, 'Everyone says that until they get a heart attack!' That was enough to shock me into a more co-operative frame of mind, but the frustration was enormous. I still found it difficult to be seriously worried about the possible dangers in view of my continuing improvement, but that was just as well given the statistics. Thousands of people a year die as a result of post-operative emboli, although new techniques are now reducing the figures. That's why it's so important not to ignore any symptom after you've had an operation, in case further treatment is needed.

In the end I had to stay another week in hospital: more eating and sleeping, but no flowers this time and no fuss. Towards the end they did let me out for an afternoon for my son's sixth birthday because I was so agitated at the idea of missing it. I was also concerned because I hadn't told some of my family that I'd been re-admitted to hospital as they really weren't in any shape to deal with this new development. So the whole thing turned into a sort of Keystone Cops with me being brought home just in time before the family arrived, then trying to make sure the children didn't say anything to give the game away, then waiting for everyone to leave and worrying I was going to outstay my 'three-hour pass'. It all sounds crazy now, but my father had developed an embolism after cancer surgery twenty years before and subsequently died. Even though I was aware how much progress had been made in that time, and how strong I was feeling, I knew that the idea of history repeating itself would add to their misery.

I was gradually weaned off the Heparin drip and onto Warfarin tablets (both are commonly used anti-coagulants) which I had to take for a further three months. Regular blood tests were done to establish the clotting time of my blood and to prevent any further problems. These tests also went on for another three months, but only once a week. None of it was any problem at all, except that I was warned of the dangers of cutting myself, but I was annoyed that the whole business was taking so long.

However, I continued to feel better and better. Books I'd read beforehand about having a hysterectomy had frightened me so much that I'd thrown them away, thinking there was no point in worrying myself in advance. They'd spoken of lengthy recovery periods, of the misery of hot flushes, mood swings and other distressing effects. Above all they spoke of the mental anguish of no longer being a 'real woman'. I'd dreaded the menopause all my life, because I'd always had problems with my periods, getting very moody and irritable a few days before, with cramps, headaches and heavy bleeding: the full disaster, in fact. I'd assumed that the irritability and depression would get worse and more unpredictable, because I'd read that the more problems you had before, the worse your menopausal symptoms were likely to be.

Yet none of it happened. Flushes were, and occasionally still are, a minor irritant, especially at night when the duvet sometimes goes off and on like a movie Red Indian making smoke signals. My skin did get rather drier. And that was it. My seesaw moods disappeared, and I think not having periods any more is one of the best things that's ever happened to me.

Of course it must be agony if you haven't had children and you still want them. I probably wouldn't have had a hysterectomy but for the cancer. But for what it's worth, it gave me no real problems at all. As for no longer being a real woman, I must be very insensitive, but for me the effects have been nothing but positive. And that's as much as I'm prepared to say without blushing.

As the weeks passed, our worries began to fade into the background. All my appointments were set for my chemotherapy, but while I was able to do more and more each day, while I could go with the children to the seaside and enjoy the lovely weather, I felt calm and confident.

Naturally there were moments when the idea of cancer would send a chill through me, especially if I overdid things and tired myself out. But looking back on that time now, I realise that I was feeling rather cocky about the whole thing. Was this all there was to it? Well, I must be pretty great, sailing through it like this. Why did people make such a fuss about it all? I was mentally preparing for the chemotherapy, deliberately psyching myself up. I'd held myself together, more or less; didn't everyone say how well I looked, how marvellous I was being? Now there was just the next six months of treatment and we could get back to our lives. It would all be as though it had never happened. Our luck had held.

# 2

# Precious Poisons

*And you're lying in some room*
*Feeling like your right to be human*
*Is going over too.*
　　　　　　Joni Mitchell, 'TROUBLE CHILD'

W e'd been told in hospital that the news was good
on all the biopsies taken at the time of the operation (little samples of tissue from surrounding
areas to be tested for cancer cells). No other cancer had been
detected, they said, and the chemotherapy I was about to start
was just an insurance policy against further disease. I had a
body scan (see p. 120), was feeling fine and went along for
my pre-chemotherapy appointment. I knew from the moment
I saw my doctor's face that the news was not good.

She told me that the body scan had shown abnormal
glands in my abdomen. The chemotherapy wasn't to be my
insurance after all; it was now vital to treat the glands themselves. The treatment and dosage would be the same as originally planned, however, so I felt less stunned than if suddenly
everything had needed to be completely changed, but it was
still a blow. The doctors had been so certain that I was clear
of other cancer that I'd started to feel that going through the
chemotherapy was just a matter of tying up the loose ends.
Now I needed it; it had to work. Somebody had moved the
goalposts just when we thought we were winning.

We had a couple of bad days after that, but gradually my

mind got to work, busily thinking up ways round this new obstacle. I told myself that I was still in better shape than I'd been before the operation – which was true. I told myself that these abnormal glands were the only traceable signs that the disease had spread – also true. Then something very fortunate occurred. I got the bill from the Well Woman clinic. My fury at this took my mind off my glands very successfully. I wrote to them with great glee telling them what had happened, and that if I'd listened to them when they told me I was fine, I would by now either be dead or terminally ill, so I had absolutely no intention of paying their bill unless they could tell me what on earth they thought I'd got for my money. That cheered me up no end, so that by the time the day arrived for my first treatment I'd got to grips with my panic and was ready to start the next stage.

It was about six weeks after my hysterectomy that I began chemotherapy. Doctors want to give you a chance to recover from surgery, but don't want to leave it so long that it increases the risk of rogue cells spreading. By the time it started I felt quite good. I'd enjoyed my convalescence 'holiday' – pottering round the garden, days at the seaside with the children, sitting in the sun. I was still on medication to guard against any new clots forming in my lungs or elsewhere, and I had to have regular blood tests to monitor the clotting time, but none of this had any effect on my general health. I started back at my part-time job, although I'm not sure I could have coped with a full-time workload. I was feeling confident and so relieved that the long fight to get some action had worked out in the end. The pain I'd lived with for so long was gone. I'd been given lots of lovely new blood packed with red cells during the operation, so all looked well.

So once a month for the next six months, I had to go back to the hospital to be put on a drip, for which I had to stay in overnight. I would be given some preparatory anti-nausea drugs some hours before the drip was started. The drip would be connected, with the bag of saline solution containing the chemotherapy drug. In this would also be more anti-nausea stuff. My dose took about an hour and a half to drip into my body, after which I'd go to sleep for the night, usually fairly successfully. Then for the next few days, I would take anti-nausea drugs at home. (For more detail on chemotherapy, see p. 124.)

The chemotherapy drug I was being given was not one of the more toxic compounds and in addition I had a new and extremely effective anti-nausea drug. I would not want to mislead anybody else about their own chemotherapy experience, but friends treated for breast cancer and lymphoma have agreed with me that we didn't feel nearly as bad as we expected. Following the first session, my main feeling was of not being quite there, a slight headiness and some faint nausea. I also became hideously constipated, but I've never found anyone else who found the same. After a few days of taking the anti-nausea drugs, I felt fine. The first three treatments, in fact, made very little impact on my everyday life. As they continued, however, the side-effects definitely built up, until by the final sessions there weren't really any normal days. The biggest side-effect was tiredness, as my blood cells got hammered by the treatment. For some reason I became very resentful of the chemotherapy itself, and it was sometimes a physical effort not to rip the drip out of my arm and run away. I'm sure that sounds a bit dotty, but it was hard to watch the drug being delivered into my system, knowing that it would make me feel grotty for days, and more than anything knowing that I was still dependent on doctors, hospitals, drugs and needles. I wanted to manage without the anti-nausea drugs, and one month did actually try it. My advice to you is – don't!

I developed a slight problem with the ends of my fingers going white and numb, so I have to be careful if I get too cold, but that is easily managed by a pair of furry boots, thick gloves and a rather stylish hat.

I and other patients I met did not lose their hair (see p. 125) although we all thinned out to a greater or lesser extent. I also lost some underarm and pubic hair, and I'm delighted to say they've never fully grown back, which is great as far as I'm concerned.

To begin with, we were able to keep our spirits in good

shape a great deal of the time. I was having chemotherapy once a month, so for the first three months at least, only a few days each month were taken up in treatment and recovery. The rest of the time I was fine, and for the most part confident that all would be well. When, after the third treatment, an ultrasound scan confirmed that the glands were shrinking, I cried with relief. That was the first time I'd acknowledged how strictly I'd been holding myself together. We were so pleased that we even went away to France for half-term to celebrate, as my going into hospital had robbed us of our summer holiday. We had a marvellous time and I felt as if I'd returned to the human race. But I was a little worried that my stomach pain seemed to be back from time to time, and a new feeling, like a little worm of sharp pain, would move across my groin very fast. When we came home, I asked my oncologist about the pain, but she was sure that it would only be an adhesion from the surgery, so we tried once again to stop worrying.

Before the next part of my story, I want to make it very clear that the chemotherapy I received worked. It did what it was designed to do, by reducing the glands in my abdomen to a normal size. And for very many patients, one operation and one back-up treatment will be all that is required to deal with their disease, as it has proved for the other patients I know best. I don't at all want to put the idea in anybody's head that chemotherapy won't work for them; in fact the likelihood is that it will be successful in eradicating all traceable disease.

# 3

# 'It's Back'

*Sisyphus was punished with eternal torment. The Judges of the Dead showed him a huge block of stone ... and ordered him to roll it up the brow of the hill and topple it down the farther slope. But as soon as he has almost reached the summit, he is forced back by the weight of the shameless stone, which bounces to the very bottom once more; where he wearily retrieves it and must begin all over again, though sweat bathes his limbs and dust his head.*

Robert Graves, THE GREEK MYTHS

We sat in the doctor's office, too stunned to say anything. The thought that kept running through my head was, 'It's all supposed to be over, they said it would be over.' I'd come to see the gynaecologist who had performed the operation to talk about a problem I thought was related to the hysterectomy, but after he'd examined me, he told us he wanted to do a laparoscopy (see p. 120) to look at a swelling he could feel in the bowel wall. I felt well; I was getting stronger every day; the chemotherapy had done its job – but the cancer was back.

It was only five months since the operation. I'd thought the worst was past, but now we were being told we had to start all over again. So, after nearly two years of illness and six months of treatment, I finally discovered how it feels to be told you have cancer. The first time I'd felt so bad for so long that I knew I had to be very ill and was so relieved when action was at last being taken that it never sank in. This time I was well, stronger, recovering – but somewhere inside the cells were growing, unfelt, duplicating silently and spreading a new tumour like some monstrous fungus over my gut.

For many days, I seemed to have no reserves of strength or will left to meet this new hurdle. After trying so hard for so long, I was back at the bottom of the mountain. I felt terribly tired, swamped by the effort to stop the screaming voice in my head which intruded into the most mundane tasks to tell me this time I was finished, I was going to die, saying over and over that I couldn't couldn't couldn't go through it all again.

All around were preparations for Christmas which seemed to mock us. I suppose all the things it stands for only underlined the fears we couldn't overcome. It was a time for families, when ours was to be ripped apart; a time for peace, when we had none. All I could think about was how my husband would manage, and how the children would be affected by growing up without a mother.

Breaking the news to family and friends was a very difficult business. All the thoughts we were trying to deal with in our own minds came back at us reflected in their eyes, and we had to fight all over again to make sure their fear didn't infect us. It was as if we'd been kidding ourselves that we'd won the war when it had only been a minor opening skirmish. I had been proud that cancer, with all the terrors that the very word awakes in people, hadn't overcome me in the past months. I'd fought it, pushed it back, thought I was safe again. I had seen my husband's relief, his lessening of tension, and the way the children had settled down once more after my weeks away. I'd even enjoyed the long lazy summer afternoons of my convalescence. Now I'd been thrown right back to the beginning again. What a fool I'd been to think I had beaten my demons. Now they came back with terrifying force.

I went through the motions of Christmas preparations and festivities, telling myself quite matter-of-factly that it would be for the last time. I felt as if I'd stepped outside my life, cut off from normal existence as completely as if I were encased in glass, and I had no control over any part of my mind. I was reduced to an assembly of cells, and yet again part of that assembly, part of my own body, was trying to kill me. I spent whole hours trying to feel physically how much bigger the growth had become since yesterday, or a week ago, as if I could get in touch with my defence system and will it to fight back. Then I would have to go back out into the world I had no part in and go through the motions of being that ordinary woman I used to be.

I went to my son's school carol concert, and we all stood together like any other family. A friend of mine started to talk to me but her eyes started to fill with tears and I had to cut her short, speaking brightly and much too fast, because I knew if I let go of the lump in my throat there would be no stopping me, and this concert was only the beginning of all the yearly rituals that I'd have to get through.

I watched my children in their nativity plays. They were so little and so excited, and my heart sank as I thought about the moment when we'd have to tell them I wasn't better after all. But then, at my daughter's nursery school show, I saw a man whose wife had died two months previously in an accident. He was helping with the play, singing and playing the guitar, and smiling for his two little sons.

I was suddenly very ashamed, and so angry with myself that I had let all my terrors take me over without a fight. I thought how far away we still were from that widower and his bereaved children. It was another of those moments when I felt a real rush of energy, and when it was easy to see the truth behind all those clichés. While there's life there's hope, there's always someone worse off than you – it was all suddenly and wonderfully real to me. My mind had absorbed the blow, and was back within my control again. Suddenly I knew I had the strength not to give up. The nursery teacher said a few words at the end of the show, and there was an encore of one song that she said had sounded a bit ragged and not very loud. All the children were to sing it again as loudly as they could. So the piano and the guitar started up, and I saw my little daughter, dressed as an angel in a white dress and tinsel, taking the instruction all too literally and yelling the words as loud as she could, which in her case is a pretty impressive decibel rate for her size. We all laughed, real proper laughter, and all at once I felt truly calm and happy. A great knot in my chest dissolved as I knew I was now ready to start again – I could always start again, because I was still part of something alive and strong.

In the days immediately before the second operation, I seesawed between this quiet determination and the panic which still broke through at bad times, but on the whole I kept that more positive feeling going. Sometimes the weight of what was coming would crush in on me, but as it drew nearer, I knew that this operation was only a minor hurdle compared with what almost certainly lay on the other side of it. I'd done the Christmas shopping, I'd even made the cake, just like any other year. The children weren't too worried that I was going to be away for a day, because they'd become used to periodic absences when I was being given chemotherapy. So at least their excitement wasn't spoiled as they wrote their letters to Father Christmas and went to the pantomime.

The laparoscopy was done three days before Christmas. As before I wasn't in any pain, and since it was a shorter, minor operation I didn't feel too bad after the anaesthetic and was easily able to go home the next morning. That was the good news. The bad news was that as a result of what he'd found, the doctor was referring me to the Royal Marsden Hospital in London and to another surgeon.

Just the mention of the Marsden made my heart sink, most unfairly, as all I knew was that it was the specialist cancer hospital. But somehow, quite irrationally, it made me feel as though there was now no way out. I couldn't fool myself that it was anything but cancer, and even though I thought I'd already accepted that fact, I was now being confronted with the absolute truth of it and it scared the hell out of me. I had a crazy vision of a sort of Dracula's castle, with flashes of lightning and ravens circling overhead. I built up the Hammer Horror image in my mind to make myself laugh, but I couldn't get rid of the idea that just the fact of this referral somehow made my condition immediately worse.

Our Christmas was subdued but still happy. As always, it was lovely to see the children's excitement and we had plenty of company. And the human mind is a wonderful thing – it can be endlessly distracted, and there's only so much wailing and gnashing of teeth it's prepared to tolerate before it changes the subject. So my memory of that Christmas is as much about my winning the game of Trivial Pursuits, in spite of the general anaesthetic three days before, as it is about fear and trembling.

We studiously ignored New Year, as we had been hoping we'd have something to celebrate. Now it was all shattered. We went to bed at 10.30 p.m. making no reference to the new year to each other or anyone else. I had three weeks to wait until the appointment at the Marsden, and in many ways it felt like a 'phoney war'. I felt better and better as the effects of chemotherapy wore off completely, and although on one level I knew I was fooling myself, I still took pleasure in being able to walk more than a short distance, revelling in my returning strength.

I filled my days with relentless activity, feverishly seeing places and people. I didn't think it out clearly but it was as if I were tying up the loose ends of my life. I'd been back at work for several months, so I had to organise that side of things for when I needed more time off, as I was virtually certain I would. I went with some old friends for a day out to Stratford, and shopped and talked frenetically, as if I were cramming as much as I could into this calm before the storm. I had my hair cut, treated myself to new tapes for my trusty Walkman, had my legs done and a facial. I might be in deep trouble, but nothing was going to make me forget the real priorities of life and arrive at any hospital for any damn examination with hairy legs!

The last night before our first appointment at the Marsden, we went out to dinner to celebrate a friend's birthday. I dressed up to the hilt, taking special care with make-up and putting on my one posh frock. I felt really good, the company was great and there were none of the awkward silences I'd been getting used to in recent days. The food was lovely, but I'd have taken more notice if I'd known it was going to be my last free-choice, eat-what-you-want-and-as-much-as-you-want meal for several years. But it was a great evening, and without any effort I was able to keep my mind off the following day and how much was riding on it, to just be myself, enjoying the chat and the jokes. I slept easily that night thanks to the wine; there were no horrors to jerk me wide awake and shaking in the small hours. I had been having more and more trouble sleeping, knowing the nightmares would be there waiting, but this time I had hours of true rest, with not a care in the world.

That night was another of the events (like the night I heard Carreras sing and the nativity play) that stand out in my journey through my sickness as having enormous influence on us. It can't have been that cut and dried, I'm sure; it must have been a combination of events and feelings which brought me back to a state of calm and confidence. But these particular moments, when I regained control of myself, when I felt contained and strong and ready to plough on again, often replay in my mind. Like my favourite relaxation techniques, I can bring out these moments and 'play them back' when things get tough, to remind me that there were always good times, even when things looked their worst. Our lives are always more than our cancer, however overwhelming the disease; we are always more than the sum of our malfunctioning parts.

Our first appointment at the Marsden was, in its own way, immensely reassuring. At the local hospitals, the fear of cancer, the awe inspired by the very word, was often almost as tangible in the medical staff as in the patients. Here, where they fought the battle every day, the atmosphere was brisk and competent. The consultant we'd come to see had an even more beautiful suit than our local surgeon, and a businesslike manner that inspired tremendous confidence. After an examination he confirmed that he could feel a definite swelling that he thought needed immediate surgery. He explained the operation, which would involve opening up my abdomen and in all probability removing a length of bowel. How much he couldn't say until he 'got in there'. Once again I was faced with a big operation and only days to prepare, as he wanted to operate the following week.

It seemed as if the endless roller-coaster ride we were on, with its highs of good days and hopeful news and its lows of disappointment and fear, had suddenly given an almighty lurch forward, and all we could do was hang on as we were catapulted forward at tremendous speed. I suddenly thought what an enormous burden these doctors must carry, with the crushing weight of hope and trust that was loaded onto them. This man knew nothing about me, except as a collection of rebellious organs, yet I was depending on him more than on any other human being I'd ever known, to fight the battle for me and give me back my life.

But this particular knight errant was jaunty and reassuringly prosaic about the whole affair. His discussion of my insides and what he would need to do was so utterly positive that it helped enormously in my struggle to absorb this latest development. I felt very cold, and as if a big stone had lodged in my throat. I remember making some pathetic joke about how my stomach would look like a game of noughts and crosses. I know I was aware of myself talking and pleased that I sounded quite normal. But inside I felt blessedly numb; the only glimpse of real fear was when I was presented with the consent form, and saw the list of possible procedures I was being asked to approve, one of which was colostomy (see p. 122). Because I knew what the word meant, it seemed to underline the gravity of what I was facing. It broke through my sense of unreality and sent a flash of sheer terror through me, so strong that I almost cried out. Everything seemed to be happening in slow motion and I was intensely aware of my hand as it took the pen and signed the paper.

I was told I'd need two days' preparation for the operation, so that gave me five days to hand over my life once more to the network of helpers who had already done so much. It made such a difference to us that when we asked them to drop the children off at school, or babysit so that my husband could come to the hospital, there was no discussion, no fuss: just help, as generous and swift as before. But this time I had to fight tremendously hard to feel any kind of optimism or energy to move forward. It was as much as I could do to stay calm for the children, and I probably didn't always manage that.

My husband and I clung to each other in our exhaustion and our fear, and that created some kind of peace for both of us. It was such a relief that we didn't need to pretend to each other. We knew, often without words, when the other needed help; we built upon each other's strength to haul ourselves towards this new and overwhelming threat.

Even now as I write this nearly two years later, I can feel the panic rising in me just thinking about that time. The pressure we were under every minute of those days was so intense that it was as if we were at the centre of a huge wind. I could hear a roaring in my ears which would build up and build up as if I would be crushed by it. I was just an ordinary person in a vast and indifferent world; could I expect to hang onto my life, when children lost their mothers every day and cancer killed one in five? Why should I be rescued?

Telling the children that I had to go back into hospital was the worst pain I have ever known. My son, who was now six, took it particularly hard, no matter how brightly I tried to explain. I tried to be reassuring without saying too much, but I had already decided that I wasn't going to lie to them, or make them promises I might not be able to keep. So when they asked when I'd be home, or would it hurt, or why was I sick again, I answered as best I could in ways they could understand. But when they asked, as I'd dreaded they would, if I was going to die, all I could say was that I didn't know; I had a very clever doctor and clever nurses and they'd all be doing their very best to make me better again.

To hear my lovely boy, just starting to move out into the world, say that he didn't want to be alive if I wasn't alive was the worst of all. We sat down and talked about all the wonderful things he could learn and do when he became a man, how much I loved him and how proud and happy he made me. We both calmed down, but it was like a line from a book of poems I remembered, something about, 'No worse, there is none: pitched past pitch of grief...' I don't know how it carries on or where it comes from, but that's how I felt as I tried to reassure him. I would do anything in the world to stop either of my children being hurt in any way, yet I was powerless to spare them this confusion and fear. They are the proudest achievement of my life, yet because of me they were troubled and unsettled.

The fear of what my death would do to them haunted my days. I had always been there for them; any work I did was built around their school hours. Now I began to regret their dependence and to think I should have taught them to be more self-sufficient. But that was crazy; they were still so young. I'd waited so long to have them that I would always have placed them at the centre of my life. Would anyone remember to put their vests and socks on the radiator in the winter mornings the way they liked? Would anyone except his father know when our son was upset, because he hid it so much?

All these thoughts and more rushed round and round in my mind; not all worthy ones either. I also joked to myself that having got me out of bed just about every night for five years between the two of them, now they wouldn't even remember me. I didn't want to think of them being influenced by any new nanny or, eventually, stepmother. I didn't want to imagine them turning into the kind of people I wouldn't recognise. I wanted my husband to find a new wife and even thought up a short list. On and on, trying to establish my authority and influence on a future I had no part in, even down to the words I wanted read at my funeral. This seemed so bittersweet at the time but now just feels embarrassing and extremely self-conscious. I can see now that I was fighting to come to terms with the idea of death, but I was consumed then with a useless guilt that I was hurting the three people I loved the best, and then I would die and hurt them even more.

I remembered that my husband had taken out some insurance when our son was born, but in our haphazard way I couldn't remember whether I was included, or what the conditions would be. So when I was alone, I searched the house trying to find the policies, to ease my mind that when I was gone there would be funds for someone to help with the children and the house until they were older. I had miserable visions of them trying to manage, but missing all the little comforts they were used to, making things worse than ever. As I searched, all I could think of was the kids coming home to an empty house, or my husband, exhausted and lonely, trying to comfort them and run the house, snatching something to eat and it all being cold and joyless. For some reason I focused on the idea of there never being any clean socks or enough milk. Why this seemed the nadir of human experience I'm not quite clear, as there are plenty of mornings when the sock supply is less than efficient, but I was comforted that the money from the insurance would at least make a difference.

Taking the children to school, I kept seeing the man who'd made me feel ashamed at the carol concert, bringing his boys to school before hurrying off to work. I tried but couldn't avoid imagining my husband in the same position, and the pressures it would put on the three of them. It all went round and round in my head while I tried to hang onto some kind of normality, and I could only be grateful that we had just a few days to wait. Again and again I tried to psych myself up into a better frame of mind, telling myself the Marsden were the experts, they'd get me through this, the surgeon had been straightforward with us. It would work briefly, as a radio with worn-out batteries will work for a minute or two when it has just been switched on, before fading out again. My reserves of willpower and optimism just didn't seem enough to help me believe in any kind of future.

On the morning we had to leave for the hospital, I kept having mad ideas that I'd run away, that I simply wouldn't go; they couldn't make me; we'd run off and hide somewhere and forget all about it. We didn't talk all that much on the journey. It seemed odd to be on a train with dozens of strangers having ordinary days, and nobody knowing what was happening to us. Even though it was January and grey skies, everything seemed in sharpened detail, like watching a travel film designed to make the most drab city look glorious. We passed all the lovely buildings along the Thames from the railway bridge to Charing Cross that I'd always meant to visit and now never would. I felt quite calm and detached, looking around at the faces and wondering what they would do if I jumped up and started shouting that I had cancer and it had come back and I was never going to see my children again.

Once we actually arrived, it was easier; we could get immersed in all the paperwork, the preparations and the information. I had to take a lot of stuff to clear my bowels out for the surgery, but it was fairly relaxed and in between times we could even walk around South Kensington, looking in all the wonderful and hideously expensive shops and admiring the architecture. I also spent a lot of time fussing about where to put all my personal bits and pieces. How far could I reach from the bed to the cabinet? Did I need tissues on the top of the cabinet or should they go inside? Every tiny thing could be discussed to decide its fate – all of which would pass another two minutes in peace and tranquillity. My husband went home that evening, which was just the start of the endless journeys backwards and forwards that he would have to make from home to the hospital.

The nurses were wonderful: all either specially trained or training to work with cancer patients. They explained everything that was to happen, including that it was policy to keep all major surgery patients in the intensive care unit for the first night after their operations. I was to be shown the unit so that I wouldn't be waking up in strange surroundings but as it turned out the unit was very busy so we couldn't go. But they told me all about what tubes I'd have coming out of where, and what they were for, and what to expect when I came round. Again we felt buoyed up by their confidence. What was so frightening to us was just routine to them, and that was very reassuring. Not that they tried to belittle our fears, but I felt they were extremely sensitive to their patients' mood swings, and knew when an airy word about the skill and reputation of the man who was about to carve up my abdomen could make all the difference to my state of mind.

Forty-eight hours is a long time to wait to do something you don't want to do in a place you don't want to be, but in the end, with help from all my distraction toys (see p. 113 on ways to kill time in hospital), the time did pass and I was waking up on the morning of the operation. This time, thank

God, I was if not first, then high on the list, and I had the pre-med injection very soon after I woke up which was wonderful. My husband got to the hospital in time to see me before I went to the theatre. As before, the theatre staff were happy to let me keep my wedding ring on (it has never been off my finger), so they taped over it. It made me feel better that there was still something that made me myself, whatever they had to do to me. Again the effects of the pre-med made me feel calm and relaxed; the time left to wait didn't seem to matter any more. Then there were more long corridors and people in green gowns and I was saying goodbye to my husband and saying in my mind the prayer I'd decided on for all of us; then a needle in my hand and then glorious and welcome oblivion.

# 4

# A Glimpse Over The Edge

*... to have my uncertain courage tested on the rack, to be reduced mentally and physically to my last component of endurance – what was going on inside me was mortal combat between my spirit and my body ...*

John le Carré, THE SECRET PILGRIM

It's hard to know what my first impressions were, waking up after my third operation. I drifted in and out of consciousness, aware only of my husband at my side and a sensation of white everywhere. I couldn't move, and was wired up to a lot of machinery. After several bouts of wakefulness, I realised I was listening for the beep-beep of the heart monitor so I'd know I was still alive. The world outside my head seemed to be in a colourless fog. I couldn't see it, but people's voices and their faces and movements all blurred at the edges. I couldn't talk very easily and I couldn't understand why it was so difficult until I realised there was a tube from my nose into my stomach.

After the operation, my husband had been told at first that there was pressure on beds, so I probably wouldn't be sent to the intensive care unit at all. But as the hours passed it became clear that all was not going according to plan, and he was told that I was haemorrhaging. I had been given an anti-coagulant drug because of the emboli I'd developed after the hysterectomy. This time I'd decided to bleed instead.

As I became more aware of what was happening, the

world shrank to the small cubicle I lay in, and the machines that beeped or hummed around me. If I had been able to move, I could have stretched out and touched the walls on each side of me. There seemed to be wires and tubes everywhere, all disappearing underneath the blankets into some part of me. There was no daylight, only artificial light which at night was only dimmed, so it was never dark. I could see nothing except the bed opposite, and I found myself wondering quite without concern if I looked as bad as the poor man opposite me. Doctors kept arriving, but nobody told me very much; they were always at the foot of the bed, far away in the fog, and the effort to call out to them, to demand that I be taken account of, was beyond me.

I don't know who told me I was haemorrhaging; the first two days after the operation are just a jumble in my mind of being half-awake, and I soon learned that if I asked for another injection of pain-killer, I'd be quite comfortable for a while and drift off to sleep, so I seemed always to be asking. There was no pain, but a lot of discomfort and I didn't want to be awake because I was afraid of the fog that seemed to surround everyone who was out there walking around and telling me things, and I couldn't reach through the fog to tell them it was there. But I knew that there was something wrong, because nurses would keep coming to look at the transfusion drip and then at the drain from my abdomen that was always filling with more blood, and then sometimes they'd remember to give me a smile or say something but more often they didn't; they would just put up another bottle of blood, and another and another, but it just kept running away, out through the hole in my side.

And they'd keep taking my blood pressure, but I knew the numbers weren't right; they weren't writing enough strokes on the chart. I knew there should be three figures above the line, but I was too tired and the fog was always there, and all the world had shrunk into this small white place. I thought that if I tried to ask them things, then I'd find out that I wasn't really there at all, that I was already gone beyond any reach of theirs, and was only watching some sort of endless action replay that I had no part in.

Those first two days are all caught up in this terrible jumble of pictures, and although now I can rationalise what I felt and realise that it must have been the deep weakness from the loss of blood that made me feel so detached, I still find it tremendously hard to allow myself to remember, because I know that nightmare vision is always there waiting for me. I was beyond any feeling other than exhaustion, beyond any reason, just a thing, a heap of flesh lying on a bed, broken, a half life, a wretched useless hulk. I had no thought, no wish, but for this cruel postponement of my peace to be over.

On the third day the surgeon came; he may have been before, but I don't remember. He told me that the bleeding wasn't stopping, and I might need to go back to theatre for another operation to stop it. The hum of noise from the machines grew louder, my head was pounding with it, and suddenly racing with terror where before there had been only apathy and inertia.

My mind scrabbled frantically to stop the rush, to keep hold of any shred of my own self in the chaos in my head. I couldn't think in any positive or coherent way; I could only keep thinking that I couldn't take any more, that I couldn't prolong the struggle through the fog and back out into the light. The noise in my head swirled round and round. There was nobody in sight; the curtains had been drawn across the end of the cubicle and I was totally alone, drowning in this swirling noise and chaos.

Then it all stopped. There was a great calm and my mind seemed to clear, as if the dull film on everything had been blown away. Into the quiet a thought came, speaking calmly and rationally that I couldn't do this any more, I was too tired. I had done all I could, but I had no more strength. Now the thing to do was to close my eyes and it would be dark and peaceful. I wouldn't have to fight any more and I could go to sleep. My eyes were closed, I felt completely relaxed, and I felt myself moving away from all the noise and the bustle – but then it was as if the thought of the children crashed into my mind, as if they were calling me as they did each morning at home, waking me up, refusing to allow me to sink into the warm darkness. And I knew that I couldn't leave the white lights and the machines, and that I had to keep on trying to break through the fog until I made it.

I don't know how real this was on an objective basis; I've never had the courage to ask how close I came, but I still believe I made a choice at that moment not to die. It wasn't even a choice I wanted, and that thought still chills me when the memories intrude unbidden into my mind. It would have been so easy just to let go, to give in to the stillness that felt so welcoming. And as that endless day went on, I came to the most frightening thing of all – knowing that I wasn't scared of dying but it was not being able to die that caused me real despair. I could do nothing to escape the fear and the noise and the endless activity which had long since seemed pointless. I had lost any hope or connection with my real life; I was just drifting, powerless and terrified, through the hours.

People kept coming and doing things to me. Men in green coats came to put a multi-line into my chest because my veins were collapsing. They leant over me and pressed the line under the skin. Then two white coats came with a mobile ultrasound, and probed to see how much blood was choking my abdomen; and still the endless tests for blood pressure. Everything ached and chafed; the roaring in my head went on and on; I was incapable of seeing beyond this hell where nobody would leave me alone and there was nothing but fear and exhaustion. I don't know how much time passed as they went through the motions of getting me ready for theatre once more, only that I longed again and again for another chance to close my eyes and stop all the terror, but it never came. I could think of nothing but making it all go away, but then suddenly my husband was there and I could hold onto him and he would help me to cling onto some memory of who I was and what I was outside this white place – that there was a whole person that I couldn't find just then, but who was out there waiting for me to fight my way back and reclaim her.

Then suddenly there was a priest at the end of the bed

saying he would give me the Sacrament. I was so scared at the sight of him that I wanted to draw away from him in the bed and tell him that I wasn't going to die; it was a mistake; I'd got past that moment and survived. But in my desperate state of mind, it seemed to me that his being there must mean that they thought I was finished, and that all they could do for me was bring the priest to mark my passage.

Afterwards I wondered if I had conjured him up, if he was part of my dreamlike efforts to make some sort of sense of what was happening to me, but my husband confirms that the priest really was there. I don't suppose he ever knew how deep and ghastly a fright he gave me. In my mind, the appearance of a priest could have only one meaning: he had come to offer the last rites. I hadn't asked for him, so he must know I was dying. I told him that I wasn't, and I could have cried with relief when he went away.

After that my memories are again fragmented, so it must have been soon afterwards that the volume of blood going into my arm was more than was draining from my side, and I wasn't going to need another operation after all. I was too exhausted to be suitably grateful for this release, but as I got a little strength back, thanks to somebody else's blood, I recall the kindness of the worried-looking registrar (I must have been getting better because I remembered he always looked worried so I didn't panic that he was thinking the worst). He patted my legs at the end of his visit and told me I would be all right.

I remember the endless patience and encouragement of a night nurse called Louise who tried and tried to help me cough up the grot in my lungs after several days of lying on my back. I was petulant and unwilling, because it hurt me to try, but she talked to me and wiped my face and brought steaming water to help ease the strain. Her gentleness and care made me cry. I was so grateful for this oasis of peace and comfort in the middle of the night, when I was alone and had to beat back the horrible thoughts and fears that came flooding in. I never saw her after that night, but I'll always think of her with enormous gratitude.

And I'll always remember too the night nurse who sat in the office talking on the phone while I tried to call again and again for the drugs that would give me a brief dreamless sleep and stop the aching and the sometimes overwhelming urge to tear myself free of all the drips and drains and monitors that held me like chains to the bed. She didn't come for ages; she didn't speak or smile, and I thought I wouldn't treat a dog as she treated me. So that made me realise I was getting better too, because two days earlier I'd have been incapable of anything so energetic as fury!

I have turned myself into a weeping jelly remembering all this. Until now, I have kept it all shut away because I have never had the courage to remember the only time in my life when I was terrified beyond endurance or reason, and if I don't keep them back, I find these memories tremendously disturbing and unsettling. But for the purposes of this book there is a point to all this angst. Only three days after the moment I thought I was dying, I was well enough to leave intensive care and return to the ward. The worst period was probably only eight or nine hours; certainly less than one day. My whole time in intensive care was only one week. Because I was totally unprepared for those feelings, they overwhelmed me. So if the same experience happens to you, I hope that in some corner of your mind you might remember what happened to me and believe it will pass.

It was horrible, but it was just a few days out of a lifetime. A few weeks later, when I came back to the hospital for a check-up, I deliberately went back to the intensive care unit. I'd found it difficult to stop the nightmares that centred around that white cubicle, and my husband had suggested I should go back there now that I was on the mend. He was absolutely right. I went in, and found that it was just a room, just a place with lots of machines. I sat on the bed where I'd spent those dreadful days, and knew that now I could deal with what had happened. The ghost was gone.

Leaving intensive care for the ward was good for my morale, because I left behind the heart monitor, oxygen mask, and the horrible nose tube which had been used to suck out grot from my stomach while I was unable to move. Three down, four to go. I found it quite heartening to track my recovery after any operation by the gradual removal of all the devices one by one, but this time it seemed particularly momentous. Back in the ward, away from the noise of the machines and the brisk, urgent atmosphere of intensive care, I felt as if I'd made great strides just by being moved from one to the other.

I could walk only a few steps at a time, but I did a dutiful shuffle along the corridor about every hour. I could soon do the whole length which seemed like a huge victory but was only about twenty yards! I was also able to have that particularly sacred and momentous ritual – the first cup of tea. Which of course tasted absolutely disgusting after a week of nothing but mouthfuls of water. What a let down; I was so disappointed. I was still on liquids only and, it quickly became clear, was totally bowel incontinent, so my first euphoria gradually evaporated in rushing backwards and forwards to the loo, and in the misery of a very sore bum! I was given some tablets to try to control these symptoms, but the stomach cramps they caused seemed worse than the squits. When I was moved onto thicker liquids, the problem worsened until I eventually got a commode next to the bed which was not that pleasant but a great deal better than a frantic dash to the loo complete with drip stand, catheter and drain, upwards of twenty times a day.

One week after the operation, the consultant did a ward round and pronounced himself pleased with the resection he had done. He told me, and his admiring students, that he had removed a length of bowel that was all tangled with tumour, and had also removed tumour from the abdomen wall. All visible cancer was gone. I don't think he said anything about further treatment at that stage, but he did remove the dressing and the staples from the incision site with a flourish! Yet another step along the way back to a wire-free existence. The drain came out the same day, so then there were two – well, three if you count the Hickman line in my chest but that didn't impede movement so I didn't – count it, that is.

Best of all, when the catheter and drip came out I was able

to see the children for the first time in a fortnight. They came rushing in, all bundled up against the winter weather, and I hugged them again and again, not wanting to let them go. They were happy and curious, and my little daughter made me laugh when she pointed to the oxygen mask on the wall, saying it was for ladies when they were having babies. When I asked her how on earth she knew that, she told me that she'd seen it on a well-known Australian soap opera – banned at home, but she'd been happily watching it at all her friends' houses while Mummy was safely out of the way. Not a lot of pining in evidence there, in fact. My son was, as before, rather more upset, but we were so pleased to see each other that I'm sure it was the right thing to do to let them come in and see that I was fine. I felt bereft when they had gone, knowing that the journey was too far for them to come regularly, but I proudly displayed the drawings they'd brought me.

As the weather worsened I tried hard not to worry about my chances of ever getting home. Already my husband had been having trouble travelling in and out of London, but as the snow fell more heavily the roads became more and more treacherous. I kept looking out of the window, and wanted to cry when I saw it was still snowing. One night I anxiously watched a woman who was waiting very late at a bus stop in the falling snow. I wanted her to come in, to be safe, as if the world outside the hospital had turned into a hostile and dangerous environment. But another part of me knew that I would be heartbroken if I couldn't go home as promised.

In the end some friends came to our rescue like the Seventh Cavalry. They had bought a Range Rover at an auction some months previously, enduring jokes and teasing as this vast machine turned up at the school gates to jostle with the more humble family hatchbacks. Now, however, they had the last laugh, because with their four-wheel drive, they could make the journey without trouble, whereas my husband's car might very easily get stuck in the snow. I was so pleased and excited that I was ready hours before I needed to be, and it felt so strange to be wearing real clothes again after almost three weeks of hospital gowns and nightdresses.

The journey home through the snow-filled streets was like a cross between a triumphal progress and my first day at school. I wanted so badly to be back home, but I felt so weak that I couldn't imagine how I'd cope. I was so relieved to leave behind the routine and clatter of the hospital, but very vulnerable away from all the reassuring nurses.

As I said when describing my first operation, I don't think there is any doubt that when you come home after major surgery you do lose some ground. You almost inevitably try to do more than you should, and rest less than when you were in hospital. But those first minutes back in your own home are such a boost to the spirits, and I'm always struck with the colour of it all. Hospitals, however hard they try, are rather dull and functional, with little to spare for frills and softening touches. Seeing all my own things and all my plants after any lengthy absence is very precious.

The children were marvellous, and had obviously been primed not to bounce on me too much. It choked me up to see the way our son would keep checking in those first days that I was still there; when he was picked up from school his first question was always, 'Is my mum at home?' I could only guess what these past months had done to the children. Our son was only six, and he had to worry about the most basic things in his life. Our daughter was still at nursery school, and was being looked after in the afternoons by the same good friend whom she'd known virtually all her life. This didn't seem to bother her, but I was hating the fact that even though I wasn't away from them any more, I still couldn't look after them.

I slept a lot in my first days at home. What bliss it was to be back in my own bed, in the dark and in silence. I tried to go out at least once each day, although the snow was still thick on the ground and rather slippery for me in my nervous and giddy state. On my first day, I walked about twenty yards from our front door to join my husband and the children tobogganing down the slope to the local pond on plastic bags (much faster than sledges, as of course you know). I felt very proud of myself, even if a bit shaky, and more importantly it was like being part of the family again. The smiles on their faces made it more than worth the effort, although by the time I'd walked home, leaving them to it, I wanted to lie down again.

My second trip was a couple of days later, in a friend's car to the local shops. I wanted to buy my husband a Valentine card. I'd never missed getting him one in nearly twenty years and I wasn't going to quit now. The pavements were quite icy and I felt horribly out of control. It surprised me that, having longed to get out of the place, I now hungered for the safety and dependability of the hospital. I felt so bad, mentally and physically, and I think this was highlighted by being back in what ought to be my normal surroundings. I'd known in theory that I wouldn't be able to take my usual hand in running the house and sorting out what the children needed for their daily lives, but when in practice I was so frail and useless it was hard to bear.

I did feel satisfaction in small victories like the Valentine card, and I tried to build on them as the days passed. But there seemed to be no lessening of the congestion in my side caused by the clot left by the haemorrhage; my gut was still tremendously irritated, and I was still so weak I often felt my eyes pricking with tears of exhaustion and self-pity. By the time I'd been out of hospital six days, my husband thought it was time to call the doctor. He came, examined me and listened to what had been happening. I wanted to shout at him, 'So it wasn't constipation like you kept telling me, was it?', but he looked tired and cold and it would have made me cry again anyway, so I didn't say anything at all. Even when he said that he thought I should be re-admitted to the Marsden.

The next few minutes seemed like hours as my battered spirits tried to accept the news. I couldn't bear to imagine what effect this was going to have on my husband and the children; their tension had lifted so obviously in the days I'd spent at home and now the screw was being turned again.

After the doctor left to phone the Marsden and make the arrangements, I had a bit of a cry and kept on saying to myself, what was I going to tell the kids? It was getting late in the afternoon so I had to get myself into some sort of shape to tell them briskly and positively that I had to go away again, and try to keep them from seeing the utter desperation I was feeling. I had to ask my poor old husband over the phone to come home from work, as I just couldn't bear the idea of anyone else taking me into London to the hospital. I can still hear the sound of his voice as I told him, its flat tone of exhaustion and worry. He had lived under the most immense pressure for so long; he'd kept the kids safe and reassured; he'd rushed backwards and forwards into London to see me every day for weeks as well as going to work; and just when we'd thought he might now have time to draw breath, we were hurled back into the fray. I thought bitterly of the tales I'd read of couples being drawn closer together by facing cancer shoulder to shoulder. At that moment, I thought the only new closeness we seemed to have found was the dubious pleasure of knowing exactly how awful the other was feeling. He had been wonderful, never letting me down for a second, but I would gladly have given up all that support for the sake of never again having to see his face looking sad and beaten as we gazed at the wreckage of our lives.

I knew I had to try to work myself back into some kind of zappy frame of mind before he came home, so I went to have a bath. I shaved my legs in a defiant sort of way and in those moments was born a sort of hot blues number of my own composition entitled, 'They Say She's Dead But She Won't Lie Down', which I deliver more Bessie Smith than Billie Holliday but you get the picture.

I don't think we spoke very much, if at all, on the trip back to the Marsden. We each knew what the other was thinking – all of it bad – so there wasn't any point in agonising over this new development, or what the implications might be.

When we arrived back on the ward I'd left so hopefully less than a week before, I got a hug from one of the nurses which nearly set me off weeping, but I could have kissed her. I couldn't have borne it if they'd been all brisk and hearty with me. Everything was very downbeat as I had all the re-admission tests; then all we could do was wait – we were getting good at that – for the consultant's round.

When he arrived we braced ourselves for the verdict. But as before we were reassured by his calm and confident manner. The blood clot was not, as he had hoped, starting to disperse spontaneously, but there were no other obvious complications. I said, 'So it's not a major panic?' and he grinned at us and said with supreme authority, 'Oh, it's *never* a major panic!'

He was reluctant, in the circumstances, to operate again unless absolutely necessary, so he wanted me to wait a while to see if the clot would start to disperse after all. I have to say I didn't take this terribly well. We were obviously relieved that nothing had gone disastrously wrong but it was very hard to be back in hospital with nothing to do but wait. The next couple of days were enlivened by a thrilling ultrasound scan and the arrival of a couple of meals (ordered by the previous occupant of the bed) of such mind-boggling ghastliness that I would never under any circumstances have considered eating them, even if one forkful wouldn't have automatically guaran-teed about twenty-seven visits to the loo. But apart from those incidents, I was beginning to go distinctly stir-crazy. Everyone who had been on the ward with me before seemed to have gone home, which made me feel even worse. I was very uncomfortable, and in no mood to try to deal with it, so various drugs were prescribed which I suppose passed a bit more time. But I did feel better when one of the sisters said, 'We should never have let you out in the first place.' It seemed as though that made this recent development not so much a new problem as an extension of the old one. A fine distinction, perhaps, but it helped.

So I was left very much on my own as we all waited for something to happen. There were constant checks to see if the clot was doing anything interesting, but it stubbornly refused to do anything at all, and I became more and more anxious as to what this fresh absence was doing to the children. I think the nurses must have realised I was about to start climbing the walls, because I had a visit one morning from an art therapist, a very nice lady with a trolley full of materials, who wondered whether I might like to take out some of my tension on paper.

I've never been particularly drawn to painting, but I was happy to have a go. However, what came out was very strange and I had to stop because I was becoming too upset. I drew a group of four little figures, blobs really, but one of the figures kept getting drawn into a sort of black scribble, until by the fourth or fifth drawing the figure was virtually obliterated and the three remaining figures were quite far away from it. I hadn't meant to do anything like that, and as I saw myself disappearing beneath thick black paint, I had to pull out of what I knew was a dangerous and negative train of thought. So I thanked the lady very much but said I didn't want to do any more but could she give me some felt-tip pens and some paper. And I spent a much happier hour doing some silly pictures for each of the children, with some of their toys, cartoons of what I knew they'd been doing, some little messages and lots of our special jokes. When my husband took them home that night they were thrilled with them, and in fact my son still has his on his bedroom wall, so my artistic endeavour was much better spent in that direction.

Eventually, after a CT scan (see p. 120) to see exactly what was going on, it was decided that they couldn't wait any longer and I needed yet another operation. I was glad something was happening at last, but once the decision had been taken it was all so quick that I didn't even get my pre-med. This just about seemed to put the tin lid on it – the only enjoyable bit of the whole process and I missed it.

When I came round properly from this fourth, though minor, operation, I seemed to be more comfortable, although I could have screamed to realise that I was once again, inevitably, catheterised and dripped! The operation had broken up most of the clot (which was huge) and the rest of it started draining away through a small incision so that after a few days, when I was scanned again, it was clear that finally the clot was dispersing. After a week I left the hospital, with a warning to watch how the blood flow progressed, and instructions to present myself a week later for a post-operative check and yet another scan.

# 5

# The Road Back

*No matter how anxious you are, no matter how obsessed,
eventually your mind will wander and you will find yourself
thinking about something else, fuse-boxes . . . the most incon-
sequential thing in the world and not your anger or illness or
the awfulness of things, not the all-consuming problem at all.
And it is that wandering of the mind that keeps the heart and
soul from drowning. That is how you learn to live with it,
whatever your particular 'it' is.*

Clare McIntyre, MY HEART'S A SUITCASE

B y the time I came home, I was so worn down by the
whole endless business that I didn't seem to have any
energy left to feel glad or relieved. I certainly had no
confidence that there would be no more complications. I had
to make several trips back to the Marsden for check-ups, which
added to my weariness, although at least I knew I was progressing.

Day after day I felt utterly drained and hopeless, and much
as I tried again and again to haul myself out of this trough of
misery, it seemed that I had no reserves to call on.

The interval before I started radiotherapy is another time
that I recall with great reluctance. Although I now realise that
it was only in fact about six weeks, in my memory it has always
seemed an endless time of grey clouds and desperate weakness.
My days were spent going backwards and forwards to the
loo, then having baths to ease the pain caused by the continuous violent scouring in my guts. We had no bidet, as there
had been at the hospital, and I remember one morning I went

to the loo six times in an hour, getting in and out of the same bath each time, feeling like a sick animal that should mercifully be put down.

I had a pre-packed liquid diet which tasted disgusting and only made me go to the loo even more; solid food was out of the question. All my life I'd wanted to be thin; now I had no spare flesh anywhere and looked ghastly. I slept a great deal, but I kept waking in nightmares and panic in which the past weeks played over and over in my head. When anyone came to see me, they appeared to be lit up from behind. Like people on a stage, they seemed to inhabit a different world, while I looked out from somewhere deep inside a weak and cumbersome body that didn't work any more. They were out in the world getting on with all the things I'd taken for granted: boring, endless jobs like washing and shopping and housework that I would have given anything for the strength to do myself. I would be exhausted by their company within minutes; I was indifferent to news of the world outside that used to be my world too; I couldn't be bothered to answer the phone. I wanted to talk to the children but very quickly their energy and noise wore me out. I longed for my husband to come home from work because he at least had shared the nightmare with me and could see what I was feeling, but when he did come I couldn't bear the worry in his eyes, his hope each day that finally I'd be feeling better. I took pain-killers just before the children came home and just before I expected my husband, so that I'd seem as well as I could be when they came through the door, but the lethargy and emptiness would creep back and I had no fight left in me to keep them at bay.

This went on for day after day, week after week. I started to feel more and more that I had finally lost my battle with cancer, and that my lack of improvement was proof that this time I was not going to recover. I started to feel quite matter-of-factly that if I was going to die it would be easier for all of us if it happened at once, rather than lingering on in this half-life. I hated the dependence of it all, the effort required to perform the smallest task. I was so afraid that I would end up as a constant drain on my family, that we would end up hating each other because I couldn't play any part in their lives in the outside world, while they were tied to the wreck of the wife and mother they had known.

It was all so different from my first convalescence, when I'd enjoyed myself immensely, pottering round the garden and sitting in the sunshine. Also, I'd been so ill before that first operation that after it was over I'd felt better than I had for months, and even the confirmation of cancer and the months of chemotherapy hadn't produced anything like this dull despair. The winter was coming to an end, the snow disappeared – but I felt I was making no progress. I seemed to have moved so far away from anything I recognised as myself, and that was what scared me the most, making me feel that I had passed beyond hope of recovery. I had no experience of protracted depression, no experience (don't laugh!) of ill health, to give me any sort of understanding of the state I was in – this feeling of complete futility, complete absence of interest in or power over living any longer. I would never have believed that I could feel like that, or that ideas and thoughts which seemed so totally alien to my nature could have taken possession of me with such force. I gradually lost all hope that I was going to live in any way other than this physical and emotional inertia, and my greatest fear was that it would go on too long.

I had been given a lot of pain-killing drugs, prescribed to relieve the discomfort of the blood clot. The drugs had been changed twice because of my reaction to certain analgesics, so I had quite a collection. I found myself wondering quite dispassionately on several occasions whether it would be easier on us all if I just swallowed a couple of handfuls and finished it. I knew I had more than enough powerful drugs to do the job. But I couldn't work out whether my husband would know what I'd done, I couldn't decide whether anyone would investigate what had happened, and I couldn't bear the idea that his pain should be added to by knowing I had given up trying.

My memory is that these mad thoughts seemed perfectly rational. I didn't want anybody upset, but I could not bear any more, and I was considering what to do as calmly as if it were a matter of what to wear that day. I remember wishing bitterly more than once that I'd simply closed my eyes and given in to the blackness I had glimpsed in intensive care. But I hadn't given in to it, and sometimes I felt I had to stick it out for the same reasons I'd felt then, but there was more than one day when this train of thought ground through my mind relentlessly.

Describing it now, I still find it unbelievable that values I thought were most basic to my character were simply overturned while I lay marooned in this endless despair. The person I used to be had always considered suicide to be a terribly selfish action, almost an act of aggression, and certainly as something it would be impossible to contemplate or understand. The person I used to be would never have believed that such total emptiness and apathy could take her over without resistance.

I have a good friend who has known me since our first children were bumps on our fronts. She had supported me in every way through all the highs and lows of the past year, and now when I was so low she would appear regularly, impervious to apathy and gloom, to encourage me in taking slow, awkward walks out of the house and over the common.

One morning, as we walked, I told her of these feelings that I hadn't been able to master, that I really believed it would be better for my husband and the children if I could die quickly instead of hanging on in this useless state. Instead of trying to soothe or humour me, I was surprised to find that she was really angry. She told me that the kids didn't care what state I was in as long as I was there; that I had responsibilities and that I owed it to them to hang on whatever happened and however long it took. I had no right to act as if there were any question about it, or as if the decision lay in my hands.

When I remember that scene now, it always makes me smile. She is tiny and blonde, always impeccably dressed, but she was so cross that day that I think if she were not such a lady she would have stamped her foot. I quailed at an unexpected attack from someone who had always supported me so much. I think she was too shocked by the enormity of what I was saying and the prosaic way I was saying it to feel much sympathy for the depth of my misery, but her outrage gave me a much-needed jolt. Self-pity can be surprisingly addictive and I was wasting energy in wallowing in how dreadful everything was – energy I could put to much better use. My friend's kick in the pants may not have changed things immediately, but I've always felt that at least it gave me a shove in the right direction.

I hope I've shown by remembering all this misery just how unrealistic it really was. I hadn't thought enough beforehand or prepared myself sufficiently for the impact of major surgery. Once I was in the pit of despair, I was in no condition to view the situation with any objectivity. I had undergone four operations in eight months. I'd had pulmonary emboli, chemotherapy and a haemorrhage that needed nine units of blood, more than a bodyful, to stop it. I was unable to eat enough to build up my strength and I had constant diarrhoea, which was a further drain on my limited energy.

*That* was why I felt the way I did. Not because I was dying, or cracking up, but because my body had been through the wringer. There was probably no way I could have felt any different. But if there had been somebody to say all this to me, if I had been warned of the impact of the surgery, I might have felt I had something to hang onto, and more able to take each day as a step along the road back to strength. But no one in the hospital had given us any information about the impact of the abdominal surgery and I simply hadn't expected it. My hysterectomy had produced nothing like these symptoms. But of course the hysterectomy, although a major operation, did not involve any organ needed for the actual business of keeping me alive. I could do without a womb, but I couldn't do without a bowel, and my body's efforts to mend itself therefore took that much longer.

During this period I was in such a low physical state that my mum stayed most of the week with us, taking charge of the children and the meals. I was so grateful for her help and support, but it also made me feel like a spare part in the household, a miserable figure in a dressing-gown who appeared from time to time for short periods before disappearing back upstairs. That was something else I needed to give myself a kick about. I started to get up and get dressed, instead of spending hours and hours just lying in bed. Even if I went back to bed within the hour, the act of getting myself ready for the day was important. And if I couldn't cook a meal, I could still peel some vegetables, or make a shopping list.

As spring started in earnest, I began to get out a little bit more. I was determined to be active enough to walk our daughter down the path to her new school on her first day. When it came, we all went together. As I watched her march off into her new classroom without a care in the world, I felt sad about all the time I'd missed with her, but proud that she was confident enough to breeze into school quite happily. That was at the beginning of April and a few days later I started radiotherapy. Like Frank Sinatra, this turned out to be the start of my umpteenth come-back.

# 6

# My Very Own *Star Wars*

*We have to concentrate all our firepower on the points we know to be vulnerable. Only by destroying the Death Star can we defeat the Empire and the Dark Side. May the Force be with you.*

STAR WARS

F or me, the experience of radiotherapy was like taking part in a science fiction movie. Even after all the machinery I'd already encountered, which beeped or blinked or moved me about, this was something else again. But, as with the treatment, the waiting and all the other trappings of cancer, I got used to it very quickly and, like the operations and the chemotherapy, it wasn't as bad as I'd been led to expect.

The initial preparations were rather intimidating. It made my heart sink to be measured and marked for the treatment, rather like a sacrificial victim. But this preparation only needs to be done once and the staff were very friendly and reassuring, talking to me rather than at my abdomen. (See p. 126 for more information.) This first session certainly seemed to take quite some time, as accuracy is crucial and things are checked again and again. Relaxation techniques helped me quite a bit with this (see p. 100), and I kept myself amused by imagining my body as starring in one of those deeply unconvincing movies in which the spaceship or submarine is shrunk to microscopic size to perform some incredibly intricate and dangerous operation in miniature. The radiotherapy waves

54

were going to be the good guys, travelling at supersonic speed to zap the evil forces and make the world safe again. Well, I know it's pretty pathetic but it worked for me, even if it only made me giggle at how my brain as well as my body was being scrambled by all these processes.

The initial preparations don't need to be repeated, so each actual treatment was very short. I had radiotherapy daily for five weeks. My first confrontation with the treatment room caused a few gulps – the machine was huge, in the middle of a big empty space and looked like something out of a Bond film; the room where the operators sit looked like Mission Control – but when I considered the fact that all this technology was working to make me better, it was rather reassuring.

For each treatment I climbed onto a bed-type platform jutting out from the main machine. I was carefully positioned as I was having treatment from four directions. The machine moved, so I didn't have to, and was set to my 'frequency'. Everybody then left the room! The first time this happened I felt as if I were two years old and had lost my mum in the High Street, but the operators simply can't be exposed to everybody's dose of radiation, and if you think about it it's only the same as an X-ray. If I wanted anything, the staff would be in contact with me via microphones. Then when everything was ready they told me to keep very still. A gentle buzzer sounded while the machine was actually in operation, so I knew how long to hold my breath. But as each treatment time was so short, I found it easiest just to breathe normally, then stop when I was told to, rather than take a great gulp of air which only made me more tense. Each of the four bursts took about ten to fifteen seconds (they weren't vague about it, I am) and that was it.

After two or three goes at this, I was quite blasé about the whole thing. I'd walk in, pull my jumper up and my trousers down, and hop on the bed like an old hand. All that bothered me then was the inevitable waiting time, but I always came prepared with something to read, popped off to France in my mind or chatted to the other people waiting, as I often saw the same people every day. We would natter about how we were feeling (useful if you're all at different stages), moan about the waiting and make general small talk. The only drawback to this socialising was that occasionally there would be somebody who wanted to wallow in every ghastly detail of their whole cancer experience, making it sound as though the radiotherapy was some horrible torture invented by the staff specially to distress them, and who could see nothing good or hopeful in anything.

To an extent I could sympathise, as we all have black days and when you talk to another cancer patient you know they really do understand. I was happy to try to help to a certain extent but if it went on day after day, I'm afraid I got angry. There was no choice about turning up for treatment every day, so their continual carping seemed a waste of energy. We were all in the same boat, so we should be trying to support each other, not adding to each other's problems. In the end I stopped listening, or I'd walk up and down outside the waiting-room. I felt I already had enough to deal with, and I reacted to these moaners just as I had to wailing friends and relations. Confronted with those who seemed determined to whip themselves up to the point of very loud and obvious hysteria every damned morning, I had no patience. I did have it out with one patient who was near my own age, and it did the trick. She admitted the extent of her fear and in the end we helped each other. But it was often the elderly patients who complained the most, and I felt they probably had the right, so I tended to avoid their doom-laden conversations rather than object.

These wailers unsettled me and were bad for my morale. I found myself remembering the sort of women who insisted on telling you for years after childbirth how many dozens of stitches they'd had; how excruciating the pain had been; how many hours, days or weeks they'd been in labour and so on and so on – instead of focusing on what it was for, which was their child. So in the same way, instead of getting bogged down in the inconveniences of my journey to the hospital, or the side-effects of the treatment, I tried to focus on the aim of the exercise, which was to keep the rogue cells at bay.

The side-effects I experienced, like those of chemotherapy, were less severe than I'd expected. And as with the chemotherapy, it was the tiredness that really got to me, except that this time I was recovering from a major operation, plus the haemorrhage and its complications. But I was now starting to feel stronger, and didn't find that the radiotherapy knocked me back to any great extent. Because I was being treated in the area of my abdomen, my bowel incontinence was aggravated, but not enough to stop me feeling that at last I was making some progress. Diarrhoea can be a side-effect for patients who are being treated in the abdomen area, but I found that if I didn't eat before the treatment I could make it to the hospital and back without, er, . . . incident.

As the weeks of treatment passed, the tiredness began to build up as it had with the chemotherapy. Most days, I slept in the afternoons. I sometimes felt a little queasy, sometimes headachy and a bit low or depressed – but whether this was really the radiotherapy or more due to a combination of post-operative effects and the strain of travelling to and fro, I don't know. Anyway, the side-effects weren't bad enough for me to spend too much time thinking about them.

Hair loss will occur in the area of treatment. For some reason I also lost the hair in my armpits again, but this seemed to me some sort of recompense for having to have the treatment. Obviously if you need treatment to the head, the impact of hair loss is more stressful. Hair usually grows again, but I do know one woman who after brain surgery, chemotherapy and radiotherapy to the head, remains (very unusually) bald after two years. While I don't want to belittle the emotional impact of hair loss on those who experience it, I feel her attitude is very practical. She is glad to have recovered from a very dangerous condition and that is her priority. She had a very long fight back from her treatment; in fact for a long time it seemed that she would always be slow in her speech – which was often frustrating for her and agonising to watch – and awkward in her movements. But the last time I saw her, she was transformed, her old self once more. It was truly like a miracle. She had us all in fits with her story of a woman who'd been chatting to her and who asked my friend how she kept her hair in such good condition, as the woman's had been dull and awkward since the births of her children. My friend had then proceeded to tell her that her lovely shiny hair was in fact a NHS synthetic wig! They both collapsed laughing about this, although my friend said that she'd never tell anyone she thought might feel embarrassed about it. She doesn't bother with a wig at home, and she told us that everyone who comes to the house, like the postman or the milkman, is quite used to it.

To see her so much better was the most tremendous boost for me and the other people who met her that day. One woman who'd been very afraid of losing her hair when she was having chemotherapy felt particularly comforted by her matter-of-fact attitude. I felt it was another example of how we can never give up hope that more improvement is possible, even when it seems so long since treatment finished.

I want to say again that I don't want to minimise the distress felt by people who lose their hair, but she is simply the only person I know personally who did go bald – and she won't let it beat her.

Although some people are restricted on bathing, I was able to have brief showers, which was good, and as I have quite dark skin I didn't find that my skin was sore, though it was slightly irritated after the shower. Fairer-skinned friends had rather more of a problem, but nothing too dreadful. I did find my scars itched while I was having treatment and for some time after, probably because the new skin of the scar was more susceptible to the radiotherapy rays, but a smear of Vaseline seemed to deal with that. When I started swimming again a couple of months later, I found the chlorine in the water had the same effect, so I still try to remember the Vaseline and pretend I'm oiling myself up, getting ready to swim the Channel. I was also told to keep the treatment area out of the sun completely when on holiday for the first couple of years.

I was very lucky with travelling to and fro for the radiotherapy because a kind bunch of friends drove me. I needed help as I was still too weak to drive or travel that distance on my own, and also had the loo problem. But other people I know went the same distance or more, quite happily driving themselves or going by train. It was the effects of the operation, not of the radiotherapy, that made this impossible for me.

On the last day of treatment I felt wonderful, and as I left the hospital for the last time I wanted to cheer. This time, this time, it was going to work and I'd be all right. I was finished with treatment after what felt like forever and it felt good. I handed over my parking pass to the guy in charge of the car park, told him I hoped I'd never see him again and gave him a kiss on the cheek. He did look rather startled but not displeased and he wished me all the best. On the journey home my mind was buzzing with the thought that I'd done it, I'd done it, and I had such a daft grin on my face I'm sure the passers-by must have thought I was crazy. They'd have been even more worried if they'd known I could have quite cheerfully kissed each and every one of them, as I made that blasted journey for the very last time.

# 7

# Learning To Live With Cancer

*... Frances had come to realise that [grief like] illness is unstable; it ebbs and flows in tides, it steals away to a distance and then comes roaring back, it torments by deception. It plays games with time and reality. On some mornings she would wake ... and feel herself purged ... and then, within hours, she would be back once more in that dark trough, ground into her misery.*

Penelope Lively, PERFECT HAPPINESS

And now for the really bad news! When I started writing this book, I realised I was beginning several chapters with the words, 'One of the hardest things about living with cancer is ...', so I've saved them for this, because starting your life again once treatment is complete really does merit this description. It's all supposed to be over, you have every right to expect to be able to put it all behind you, but I'm afraid I felt more alone and vulnerable than ever, with a sense of hopelessness that after all we'd been through we still couldn't return to a normal life.

I realised that everything came into my personal time scale of BC and AD – before cancer and after diagnosis – and I went through a period of what I now think was true bereavement. I had to mourn the person I'd been before I got cancer, because there was no way back to being that person. The happy positive woman who'd never given more than a fleeting but confident thought to the future had gone for ever. The life that had run quietly but smoothly, in which things always seemed to work out for us, seemed a hollow joke. Everything was coloured by my cancer; it was never out of my mind.

I was haunted by memories of the past year: the first time I was told the diagnosis; the hope bitterly destroyed when the cancer came back; the seemingly endless days in intensive care and my pitifully slow recovery from the surgical and chemical war waged in my body against the rogue cells.

As endless and demanding as the round of hospital appointments and treatment sessions had seemed, when I had finally finished with them I felt paradoxically as if an enormous support had been withdrawn. Now, instead of being given reassurance every couple of weeks, I only had check-ups every three months. In between, we were on our own. And while I was moving from one stage to the next, or even one crisis to the next, my days had had a momentum of their own, and I was able to pace myself from one step to the next. Now, with the relief that treatment was over came a rush of fears and images I'd kept at bay while I took each obstacle as it came. More than anything, the fear of further recurrence kept blasting into my mind.

At the same time, I did keep reminding myself how far I'd come. Even while I'd been having radiotherapy, I'd been improving. Not so much physically, but my mind was daily more and more free of that hideous dullness in which everything seemed hopeless. I began to develop a routine to deal with my bowel problems while allowing me to get out of the house a bit more. If I had someone to drive me I began to go down to school to collect the children. We even went on holiday six weeks after I finished radiotherapy. I was tired, certainly, and had to miss out on all the lovely holiday scoffing, but I was there, I was part of it.

I passed the summer alternating between feeling good that I was undeniably getting stronger, and feeling bad that I couldn't seem to deal with the worry of each and every little pain that lasted more than a day. What made it worse was that the pain always seemed to be in the same place as the original ache which had turned out to be cancer. In July I went to see the consultant who had performed the hysterectomy, because the pain had been there for nearly a fortnight and I'd worked myself up into a bit of a state about it. When he examined me and said there was nothing there, I felt like crying with relief and came away from his office feeling determined to get the better of my worries. I did quite well as the summer went on. The children were out a lot during their school holidays, which took pressure off me and left me free to recover at my own pace, which was so slow I sometimes wanted to scream with frustration, but nevertheless I was always moving forward. We had days by the sea, picnics and walks, and slowly I could do more and more.

I was so confident in my recovery that when school started for a new year I volunteered to help in the classroom, something I'd always meant to do once both children were at school full-time. I did a few mornings, but was depressed to find that I had been too ambitious and was becoming exhausted by it. And I'll never again think teachers have a good deal with all those holidays. They need and deserve every minute of them. I was very upset by this setback, and saw it as a measure of how far I still was from a normal life. Looking back on it from another year on, I think I was just being impatient, but I'd been ill for so long that I was becoming more and more thoroughly fed up with the snail-like pace of my recovery. At the same time I took pleasure in the things I could do for myself. It really was like being on an endless roller-coaster ride; each day held its ups and downs.

One Sunday in October, we went out for the day to Dover. As we went round one of the town museums, I began to feel quite strong cramps. It was not that unusual, but they didn't go away and on the way back the pain became quite severe. When we got home I had a hot bath, hoping that the heat would relieve the cramps, but still great waves of pain were clutching my abdomen. I went to bed with a hot-water bottle, but the pains didn't get any easier, and in the end my husband called an ambulance.

By the time it arrived I had become very agitated, and in my panic I'd started to hyperventilate, getting too much oxygen into my system and making myself light-headed. The ambulance man, thinking I was having a heart attack, gave me more oxygen which made the problem worse. I was petrified as I saw my hands turn blue and twist themselves into impossible contortions. By the time we reached the hospital, I had abandoned any attempt at keeping my conscious mind calm and controlled and was virtually delirious. Far away in the back of my head I kept thinking, 'This isn't fair, I'm going to die now and it's all been for nothing.'

But once we were in the Casualty department, a nurse talked to me very quietly, telling me there was nothing they could do till I calmed down, and giving me a paper bag to blow into to establish a breathing pattern and so break off my hyperventilation. Although I was pretty far gone, I did realise that she couldn't think I was about to die if she was handing out paper bags and telling me to relax! It took me nearly an hour to take control of my mind and my breathing, made more difficult because the pain was as sharp as ever. I could hear my husband telling the Casualty doctor all about the treatment I'd had, and I knew I was being examined. I was taken down to X-ray – I suppose they were looking for a blockage in my bowel – but all I could think about was the pain and my desperation at being back in hospital again after coming so far.

After a couple of hours I was transferred to another hospital, and we had more questions to answer. By then it was the middle of the night, so it took some time to find a doctor on duty, but after what seemed like forever I was given a large, wonderful dose of pethidine which sent me to sleep and away from the pain.

When I woke up five hours later, I was still in pain but it was more localised and not so severe. More importantly, I felt much more in control of myself and ready for whatever happened next. After waiting endlessly for a visit from a consultant on his rounds, I was enormously relieved to be told that there was no apparent bowel blockage; in their view the pain was due to a twist in the gut which would untwist itself when it was good and ready. Meanwhile, I would continue with the pain-killers and not eat or drink again until I'd been to the loo, so they could be sure my system was working normally – well, normally for me anyway.

I started to feel rather foolish, and I knew I'd unquestionably made things worse for myself by hyperventilating to such a degree, but the pain had been so bad that I just hadn't been able to grab hold of myself and work my way through it. I probably wouldn't have been able to manage without the heavy-duty drugs in any case. But of course it's one thing to get into hospital – and quite another to get out again. After thirty-six hours I was feeling quite okay again apart from the cramps, but even after I'd been to the loo they decided that I had to have a meal and wait for that to get through the gut to make sure the twisted section had now unravelled itself. More hospital food, more sleepless nights because of the noise, more hours to pass.

For me, that whole episode was the last straw. Afterwards, I found that all my worries started up again with greater force. I was very tense, and very frightened that these spasms would become a regular event. My sleep problems grew even worse, and I became more and more reluctant to go to bed, because I knew what horrors were waiting in the dark – the panic that would spiral up no matter how hard I struggled to control it, until I could hear the rush in my ears like a wind roaring in a chimney and feel my heart start to pound. I would get out of bed, prowl the house or read endless trashy novels until some sort of calm would return and I was so heavy-eyed I knew I could probably fall asleep before the monsters got hold of me again. Because I became so tired in this way, I was less able to improve in the days that followed. It was a vicious circle and although I had managed other setbacks, this comparatively trivial episode seemed to have overwhelmed all my efforts towards a return to my normal life.

The tension in me grew even worse as preparations for Christmas began in earnest. Everything reminded me of what had happened the previous year, and memories of those terrible weeks played themselves over and over in my mind. The crunch came when I went along to the children's nativity play. I started to feel edgy straightaway as I remembered the year before, but thought I would be okay once it got going. Every year, there is a collection for charity after the performance, and the children themselves decide which charity they want to support. When the headmaster announced that this year they had opted for Cancer Research, I couldn't bear it. The idea that children so young knew that there was such a thing as cancer at all seemed cruel, and thinking of all the children who had been through the distress that my own son and daughter had known just about finished me off. I had to leave the hall and run up to the empty staffroom where I could have a good cry in peace. When I'd calmed down again, I sat in the quiet and knew I had to face facts. I'd done my best, but I was not dealing with the pressure or the constant fear of recurrence that had plagued me. I was out of control, and I needed help.

To begin with, we asked the oncologist I'd been seeing for advice; it turned out she knew a psychologist at King's College Hospital on Denmark Hill who had a special interest in cancer patients. She promised to book an appointment, which came through for January. In the meantime I asked my GP (again!) to refer me to the home-care team from our local hospice, and they phoned to make a date for a few days after Christmas.

The very fact of admitting I wasn't coping, and asking for help, actually brought me a measure of calm in itself. Christmas was difficult for my husband and me, but there were still outings and jollities that we could enjoy with no reservations. When the ladies from the hospice team came to see us, I was tremendously reassured by their understanding of the demons I was facing. They knew, as nobody else knew, what we were trying to fight off. I had begun to dread visits from people who so obviously wanted to believe it was all over, and had sensed their impatience with my continuing weakness. I think they felt I was being almost wilfully negative – I'd survived the treatment, the news was encouraging, so that was that, wasn't it? Once again, it seemed to me other people had no understanding, or wish for understanding, of how we really felt. But these women had seen and heard it all before. Not that they were dismissive of our feelings, but it was such a relief to be assured that thousands of people had trodden this path before us, and that they had got through in the end.

We had two helpers, one a specialist cancer nurse and the other a social worker with special training in helping cancer patients. The nurse was able to offer us some advice regarding the physical problems I was still encountering; the social worker listened and listened, and told me I wasn't weak or negative but just tired out. This made me cry a bit. It was as if I had been forgiven somehow, because I hadn't failed but just stumbled along the way. Above all, I drew on their confidence that I could find a way to live with myself and what had happened to me.

The next step was to visit King's and see the psychologist. We had quite a long talk, and again I became aware that my feelings were not so unusual or impossible to resolve. I remember asking him how other patients coped with the fear of cancer coming back, and he said that everyone found their own best solution. Some turned to religion, some to special diets and alternative therapies, some to tranquillisers or alcohol. I thought that I'd do best with a blend of all of them! We talked a lot about the anger and hurt I continued to feel about the added emotional burden some people had given us, and our anger that our lives were still being damaged by what ought to be in the past. It was good, and honest, and I felt as I had with the hospice team, that just being able to express some of these feelings to an outsider reduced their power to hurt me. At the end of the appointment he gave me a prescription for some tablets to relax me before I went to bed.

The hospital pharmacy was very crowded, and I was worried that if I waited for the tablets I would be late to collect the children from school, but the nice lady at the desk said I would have no problem getting the prescription reissued by my practice GP. So I left, and went the next day to the GP's, presenting the prescription to one of the receptionists. 'Twenty-four hours,' she said. 'But it just needs rewriting,' I said, 'it would only take a minute.' I explained my incontinence problem, and that it was tiring for me to get into town more than once a week (the NHS practice is fifteen minutes' drive from our house). I then got a lecture on what their system was, and that the doctors were very busy and so on and so on, all of which took ten times as long as asking one of the doctors would have done.

I was getting more and more exasperated by this, so in the end I said, 'Go and tell Doctor X, or Doctor Y, or Doctor Z that I need this prescription now, and you can also tell them that if any of them had listened to me in the first place, I wouldn't need the bloody pills!' There was a lot more muttering, and in the end somebody went to ask one of the doctors I'd named to rewrite the prescription. She came back and told me that as I didn't need the tablets until the evening, they wouldn't write the prescription now, and I would still have to come back. I couldn't believe it, but I knew if I continued to argue I'd get really upset, so I went home. But the more I thought about it, the angrier I got. It seemed I still had to fight every inch of the way. I'd fought to get someone to listen to me in the first place, I'd fought through the treatment and all the setbacks, and I was still fighting some stupid bureaucratic nonsense when I really needed help.

When I got home I rang the surgery, told the practice secretary the whole story and ended up by saying that I couldn't think of one good reason why I shouldn't take the whole thing to the Family Practitioner Committee. I then put down the phone, went into the loo – and howled. They were great tearing sobs. I don't even remember if there were any tears; maybe it was just this enormous noise, like a wolf or a banshee or anything else that howls, on and on until I was weak and blotchy and almost giggling with amazement at myself. I don't know how long I was in there; it must have been at least an hour while I kept on and on howling, for myself, and our family, and this endless business of trying to stay alive. When I came out, I was sore in my chest from the noise, and hoarse too.

And, dear reader, I've been getting better ever since!

# 8

# In Remission,
# Or The First Five Years
# Are The Worst

*At these times I feel blurred, as if there are two of me, one
superimposed on the other, but imperfectly. There's an edge of
transparency, and beside it a rim of solid flesh that's without
feeling, like a scar. I can see what's happening, I can hear
what's being said to me, but I don't have to pay any attention.
My eyes are open but I'm not there. I'm off to the side.*

Margaret Attwood, CAT'S EYE

As 1992 began, I had been reluctant to test myself in any
way, because I was afraid I'd find I was still too weak,
either mentally or physically, to make further progress
into an ordinary life. I still needed regular reassurance from
examinations and scans that there was no traceable disease in
my body. I still found it difficult to cope with the fear of the
disease coming back, to the point where I couldn't bring
myself to admit progress in case I was jumping the gun. But
with the help of my meetings with the hospice team and the
psychologist, I began to clear out a lot of the emotional dead
wood that was keeping me in the doldrums. Although I only
saw them three or four times, the fact that I could say absolutely anything to them without causing them fear or worry
meant that I started to come to terms with this new situation
of remission, and slowly began to pick up the loose ends of
my life.

I asked one of the home-care team how they managed to

soak up all the pain and fear they were confronted with and not go crazy. She told me it was like being a human sponge; they could absorb it all and then be 'wrung out' in debriefing sessions with the rest of the team, so that the weight of other people's grief didn't get in the way of helping them. I certainly found the few hours I spent with them, and at King's, of immense value.

After we had got through the 'anniversary' days – one year on from the bowel operation, one year on from coming out of hospital, and so on – I became aware that I had to stop thinking of myself as a 'patient' and as an invalid, and begin to look at myself in a different way.

One day in February I got through the post a brochure for the summer camp the children had attended for a week the previous year. I realised with a jolt that when they'd been at camp, I was already back at work (two days a week), had driven them backwards and forwards and was in charge of the house to a large extent. Now, six months later, I hadn't really got any further. I didn't go out a great deal because I was worried about getting caught with a bowel cramp, or wearing myself out. I didn't make social plans because I hadn't been able to predict how I'd be feeling from day to day. But now I was still judging myself by those measures, which were six months out of date.

I still had, and always will have, a dicky gut – but it was immensely improved. I still got tired – but nowhere near as easily. I think it is easy to get into the habit of treating yourself as delicate and fearing some relapse long after it's necessary, especially if you have been ill for a long time. And although there's a lot to be gained by a bit of cosseting and taking life easy for a while, the longer you drop out of life the more it becomes the norm. Just as I found it difficult to ask for help at the beginning, I also found it quite difficult to give it up, especially when it meant a return to the less than glamorous aspects of running a home. But if you're keeping yourself back in a passive and dependent frame of mind, it can only do harm.

You may also find that if you have been getting support from friends and relations, they too have trouble adjusting their view of your present condition. They may, from the best of motives, keep wanting to help when that help is no longer realistically needed. It can be very awkward to say no thank you, if someone has been very good to you, and you won't want to hurt any feelings, but I certainly got to a stage when I felt I had to take back my life to enable me to move on.

It's all a bit of a balancing act, between not overdoing things so that you do yourself harm, and not underdoing things. So if somebody else is still doing all the rotten jobs you really hate six months after you finished treatment – think about it!

Another aspect of moving away from the 'patient' mentality is in the amount of time you spend thinking about and talking about what has happened to you. Although such a profound and confounding experience is bound to take up the lion's share of your thoughts for a considerable time, I found that I started making a conscious effort to get some other matters into my life. I had no wish to turn into the kind of old lady on the bus who's still telling anyone who'll listen all about her operation twenty years after it happened. However ill you've been, and however much they love you, it's human nature for other people to start getting impatient and, frankly, bored if the horror stories go on too long. People have problems of their own, life moves on, and I started to feel the importance of moving on with it and not staying trapped inside the cancer experience, however overwhelming it had been.

I also found myself measuring the problems and worries of others against what had happened to us. If I was listening to tales of woe from friends or family, I would think, 'That's nothing compared to us.' From a certain stand-point it was true, but as a person living once more in the world I was actually being paid a compliment. I wasn't being treated as that person who's had cancer, but as myself as I'd always been, happy to listen and happy to help if I could. But it was actually very hard, and still doesn't always work, to start looking out-wards after so long spent focusing inwards for the sake of my own survival. You could almost say it was hard letting go of the cancer experience, as a self-righteous kind of yardstick by which to pass judgement on the foibles of others. I'd taught myself the lesson of selfishness too well, and turning it round again was sometimes painful. But other people have problems too, painful, draining or undermining problems that I had no right to dismiss.

For example, I found it tremendously difficult to deal with people who didn't seem aware of the value of their own health. The type who are always suffering from some minor ailment or another for which there seems no particular evidence. I was on holiday last year with someone like that, and got more and more resentful of what I saw as her self-obsession, and her self-indulgence in inventing more and more new illnesses for herself. It made me think of all the people I'd met who were really suffering, especially the kids in for chemo- or radio-therapy, pale and quiet and hairless. But was I really also thinking, 'How dare you tell me about illness?' as if I had some absolute standard of sickness by which anyone else's misfortune, real or imagined, was now to be judged?

Or someone would be moaning about their kids, or their husband, or the price of something or other, and I'd think how petty it all was, as if only 'those who have truly suffered' had the right to complain. So I started to smile when people said, 'I shouldn't be telling you my problems after what you've been through,' and I'd say of course I was happy to listen and that all that was behind me now. Better a reputation for saintly forbearance and extreme maturity, however little deserved, than turning into a cancer bore! Or even worse, turning into the kind of person cut off from the world around them by their inability to feel compassion.

I think I've made some progress with that, although even now when I'm told bad news, I can hear the clank of the protective drawbridge going up, keeping me safe from being drawn too far into another's life. I often feel that there isn't enough to spare for anyone other than ourselves, and I wish I didn't feel like that.

I also realise now that I was behaving very much as if there were no future to be contemplated. Not just avoiding making any forward plans, which I still find difficult, but acting as if each day were potentially final. I indulged myself and my husband in clothes and treats, justifying it time after time by saying that I deserved it. The children had to have everything they wanted to 'make it up to them'. I never wanted to have any confrontation with my husband or the children, so that they wouldn't remember any bad times. But that was still acting as a patient, not the well woman I was becoming. The result of it all is an empty savings account and a couple of kids who need a short course in fiscal reality and who have now been reminded of the true nature of Mummy's temper! No real harm done, but I don't want to spend the rest of my life on my best behaviour 'just in case' – a sort of emotional version of clean knickers in case you're run over. And when my husband and I had our first post-operative disagreement and exchanged some pithy words (about what I can't now remember), I felt great – it was back to normal!

When I really thought I was on my way back, I celebrated by booking us a package weekend in Venice at the end of February. I'd wanted to go there all my life, and it seemed the right time to do a bit of dream fulfilling. I went to the doctor I'd been seeing who'd been investigating why my gut hadn't settled down and got some powder which sets like wallpaper paste in the intestine, and which would help me to avoid bouts of diarrhoea. I tried it out a couple of times before we went, and it worked really well. If I just kept myself going with milk and glucose, I had no problems, although the effects were pretty nasty when the stuff wore off, which is a shame as otherwise I could use it all the time.

Standing up in the water taxi from the airport into Venice, watching as the buildings I'd longed to see came closer and closer, I felt like a kid at Christmas. It was everything I'd hoped it would be. We had the most wonderful time and it seemed like the start of a whole better period for us. We walked our socks off, took twenty thousand pictures, mostly of the same thing, bought the kids ghastly souvenirs and treated ourselves to a ludicrously expensive coffee in each of the mirrored rooms in Florian's. And the best thing of all was that we were just like anybody else. Apart from the odd looks from the hotel manager as I ordered another three litres of skimmed milk, nobody knew anything about us or what had happened, and it was marvellous.

So, very gradually, I began to manage my life better and better. I started making grand resolutions about this new life of mine, that I wasn't going to clutter it up with petty resentments or minor irritations; I was going to clean out the garbage and start fresh. But, this being real life, of course none of that happened. I still agree to things I don't want to do, I still put off horrible jobs until they take twice as long to do, I never did get to be that finer and wiser person all those books promised I would be. I also thought for a long time that after everything I had been through, I now deserved that nothing bad would ever happen to me again. But life, real life, isn't like that.

One of the hardest things to face was the news my husband told me later in the spring. A man we knew, who had tested clear about the same time as I had, had developed a sudden recurrence and died. My husband hadn't told me for a while, because he didn't think I was together enough, and when I heard the news I was standing at the cooker, stirring some white sauce. I remember thinking that if I could just keep on stirring the sauce and not look at him, then I wouldn't have to admit I'd been told. This man was our own age, his children were even younger than ours, and I kept thinking of his wife and how it must feel to have fought and fought with all your strength and still have lost in the end.

I felt a kind of fury too, a feeling that I was just sick of it, tired out with trying to beat it, and if cancer was going to get me in the end, why not now and get the whole miserable business over with? But as the shock wore off, I knew that I would always have to fight it, there could be no giving up, and the fury cooled into a sort of helpless sadness that our friend hadn't made it too.

If you are or have been a cancer patient, and you know someone with cancer who dies, I think at some stage there comes a sort of survivor's guilt, especially if you don't seem to be dealing with your feelings and getting back to your own life. You may feel reluctant to contact the family or friends of the person who has died, as if it would be rubbing salt in the wound because you've survived and their loved one didn't. Or you may be ashamed that you feel unable to offer any help or comfort. As in other areas of stress, you need to learn to be kind to yourself. The last thing you need to do is prove yourself worthy of surviving, but you may find that you are very much able to help because you have so much more understanding of what they've been through.

However much progress I make, at the moment I find myself unable to resolve the bitterness I still feel at the impact cancer has had on my life. My biggest regret is the time I lost with our daughter. While I was so ill, I was pleased that she was too young to be very troubled by all that happened, but now I feel very sad that I missed the last months of her littleness, and the last year when she and I should have been together before she went out into the world of school and friends. I will never have another child, and to have missed any part of her precious toddler years is very hard.

I still find that many people assume that once you're out of hospital and treatment is finished, then it's all over. So few seem to have the imagination to see the enormous emotional strain that can continue for months, and can even now catch me by surprise with a burst of fear or weeping on a bad day. And people who were least in evidence when you were at your lowest always seem to be the ones who now congratulate you as if you've now officially rejoined the human race! So these days I'm the only one who's allowed to say I'm fine, and I'm the only one who's allowed to say the worst is over. But it's true, just the same.

# PART TWO

---

# *How To Live With It*

# 9

# How Not To Be Brave

*People are capable of doing an awful lot when they have no choice, and I had no choice. Courage is when you have choices.*
　　　　　　　　Terry Anderson, freed Beirut hostage

O kay, it shouldn't happen to a dog. But it's happening to you, so you might just as well start getting on with it, any way and every way you can. Some of the pain you can't avoid, but a lot of it you can deflect or minimise.

A very difficult lesson I learned when I was starting out on my way through cancer was that, in the end, you have to cut through all other considerations and focus on yourself. You need to concentrate on your objective of getting to the other side of cancer, and abandon any excess baggage on the way. Whether this excess baggage takes the form of a friend who always gets you down, or a job that you can't finish – drop them, ignore them, let them get on with their own problems.

## EXPRESSING YOUR FEELINGS

From our earliest years, we are given messages such as don't make a fuss, put a brave face on things, don't show your feelings. For most people, the only answer to the question, 'How are you?' is 'Fine, thanks!' regardless of circumstance. This is perfectly okay for normal purposes, but an added pressure if you are actually very bad indeed. It is hard enough to realise that no one will truly understand what you are going through (except perhaps someone in the same boat), but even harder to realise that other people will be only too glad to accept your under-estimation of the scope of your disease and its impact on your life. They care about you, so they want to believe the best. But putting on a good show for others, even if the motive is to spare them pain, will isolate you even further.

You need to be able to talk about your feelings of shock and fear, to express anger at what's happening to you and to discuss your concerns about what treatment will involve. Talking helps for two reasons. Firstly, it will help to cut the problem up into manageable chunks; the more you talk, the more perspective you can get on the situation, at least for long enough to give you some valuable breathing space. Secondly, it will release a lot of the tension that inevitably builds up. If you don't feel there is anyone you are able to talk to freely, perhaps you might think of asking your GP to refer you to the Macmillan nurses in your area (see p. 135). I certainly wish I'd got help earlier.

## FEAR OF THE DISEASE

Cancer scares the pants off everyone. In a world where the fear of hell and damnation has all but disappeared, we seem to have replaced it with the spectre of cancer. As each generation passes, no matter how many advances are made in its treatment and cure, the perception of cancer doesn't seem to alter. When I was a child, the word was to be whispered; it meant agony and inevitable death. This is simply no longer true, if it ever was. Some forms of the disease are more pernicious than others. Some areas of the body are more difficult and more dangerous to treat than others. But we can all be helped in one way or another.

Only when I was within the system of cure and control did I start to get away from the unreasoning, uninformed dread of cancer and what it would mean to me, and begin to feel that I was not helpless at the mercy of this demon disease. Once I started down the path of treatment, I found I had much more perspective on the real rather than the imagined threats from cancer. I also had a lot of received ideas of what treatment would be like, which as it turned out were far more frightening than the reality. But to reach this more realistic view of cancer takes time. All I can say is try to hang in there until the first shock wears off; then you can start really making strides into dealing with your outlook and your treatment.

The first shock of learning you have cancer is a disorientating, head-spinning, agonising business which I don't think anybody can really spare you. To dress it up with words like heroism or challenge is to deny the almost unbearable pain that each day thousands of people have to endure when they are told the worst. For many of us, it will be our first contact with our most basic fears and instincts, and we are never prepared for this devastating confrontation.

So try to be kind to yourself. Don't pillory yourself for every negative thought, or bout of tears, or self-pity. See them as healing and cleansing. It's not spineless or weak or negative to be scared rigid of what's going to happen. Neither is it selfish to think, *Why me*? That first rush of emotion is entirely human and I think probably largely unavoidable. Forget whatever ideas you have of stiff upper lips and allow your feelings full rein – that way you can start all the sooner to get on with the business of collecting your strengths for the next hurdle. Because given the chance, your mind will take the problem, turn it round this way and that, have a good look at it, and chop it up into pieces small enough to deal with one at a time. It may take a few days or weeks, but it's almost as if once the tears have cleared the ground, your mind will say okay, that's enough of that, now down to work. That all sounds a bit whimsical, but it's the best way I can think of to describe the process. When I was told after my first operation that some enlarged glands had been detected on my body scan, for two days I felt absolutely flattened; I couldn't talk about it without starting to cry. On the third day, I woke up feeling brisk and in control again, willing myself forward and into believing that the chemotherapy would take care of it.

## FEAR, STATISTICS AND THE MEDIA

The deep-rooted and now actually rather outdated terror which the word cancer inspires is daily fed by newspaper reports and fictional representations of what having cancer is like, what causes it, and what it will do to you. Newspaper stories, in particular, although always describing us as 'brave', 'marvellous', 'plucky', etc, would always rather we were also 'tragic'. Bad news is what people want, they say, so that's what we get – in spades. The papers aren't interested in the long, tedious and draining fight with its small victories, devastating setbacks, and finally good outcome, which is how many people experience cancer. They aren't interested in the many ways the disease can be controlled, and worthwhile life prolonged. They want miracle cures or battles lost, black and white.

I worked for a newspaper long enough to know how a set of statistics, or a collection of pieces of information, can be presented to fit the storyline best. It's all a matter of emphasis. As far as giving you any accurate representation of the overall picture, shock reports in the papers may make your heart pound for a minute or two, but the only true story is you and your experience. Every case of cancer, every patient is unique; so don't get swamped by somebody else's tales of doom and gloom. The journalist is on the outside, looking for an angle. You are on the inside, with all the ifs and buts he's not interested in.

Very early on in my 'cancer history', I read a report in a national newspaper about a new screening programme that could detect ovarian cancer, the kind I had, much earlier. Good news, of course, but the article went on to elaborate on the present statistics for what they said was called 'the silent killer'. Leaving aside the fact that it had probably been given this name by some other journalist doing some other scare-mongering story in the past, the conclusion was that the survival rate after five years (the commonly applied yardstick), in cases where the disease had spread (as it had in my case), was rather less than one in five.

Those words haunted me and ate away at my attempts at calm and confidence. I suppose in bad moments they still do. But what were they really telling me? Statistics can't take account of the stage at which the disease was detected, the age of the patient, the strength of the patient, their quality of life, whether treatment was withheld or refused – in fact, none of the factors which make me different from every other ovarian cancer patient in the history of the world.

I am not a statistic. You are not a statistic. Two and a half years after a diagnosis of ovarian cancer, I am well, I am living my life – and who can say more than that? Maybe I am only halfway to the magic five-year figure; maybe I will still become a number on a list, or maybe I won't; maybe I'll crash while hang-gliding in the Himalayas, or maybe I'll be crushed in the rush for the china department on the first day of the Harrods Sale. 'Maybe' is a waste of time for you as you set out on this fight.

There isn't even any point in saying, avoid these stories if you can, and don't watch doom and gloom documentaries or worthy BBC2 plays 'based on a true story'.

Because there is one thing you can be absolutely sure of as far as the media are concerned, and that is that suddenly everything you read or see will be overflowing with cancer stories, all of them discouraging. And you can also be certain that the word will scream out of the page at you as an irresistible magnet to the eye. You can be reading an entirely different article, or even a different page altogether, and the word will shine like a beacon. Cancer, cancer everywhere! The most far-fetched example I found of this was when I started to read the guide to an exhibition of an artist whose pictures I really liked but about whom I knew absolutely nothing. Honest truth, the very first page I opened I saw the words, '. . . already, at fifty-seven, he was desperately ill with the cancer that would eventually kill him'.

For weeks on end, every novel I opened seemed to have a cast of characters who were either dropping like flies with cancer, or had a tragic past when the love of their life had died of cancer, or who bravely rejected the hero because they'd just found out they'd got cancer – on and on and on. It began to get ridiculous. I read several hundred pages of one novel only to find that the erratic behaviour of the estranged sister was finally explained in the last twenty pages. Yes, surprise, surprise, she knew she had cancer and had come home to die. (Not, I have to say to be scrupulously fair, of cancer, because she drowned herself in the lake that was handily placed within easy reach of her old home.) I threw the book across the room, but really the whole thing was so ludicrous that all I could do was laugh. Yes, folks – cancer can make you laugh as well!

I can quite see how it's useful to have an all-purpose way of disposing of unwanted characters, but it seems to be becoming an epidemic.

And television and films can't get enough of it either. One friend of mine, recovering from surgery for breast cancer, decided one afternoon to hire a video (something she would never normally do, which makes the outcome even more unfair) and have a relaxing couple of hours with her feet up, watching the film with her mum. She's a big Jack Nicolson fan, so she brought home *Terms of Endearment*. She hadn't a clue what the plot was all about, and sat quite happily through the gooey bits until Shirley MacLaine's daughter Debra Winger started dying of breast cancer. She sat open-mouthed in disbelief at the trick Sod's Law had played on her, and wondered what on earth either she or her mother were going to find to say to one another. We had a good giggle about it afterwards, but be warned – there is no escape. The media fascination with cancer will get to you in the end.

The biggest inaccuracy in the way the media portray cancer, and what distorts our perception of its threat, concerns timescale. Papers and television present the whole experience as if it happens very quickly, and as if one event inexorably leads to another. There are indeed cancers that are very invasive and fast-progressing. There are cases in which cancer is so advanced by the time of diagnosis that the chances of total cure are substantially reduced. But for the vast majority of us, there will be long periods when nothing much is happening, when we are recovering from operations, or having rest periods between chemotherapy treatments.

So there will probably be a lot of time – time which we can use to recoup our energies, to live our lives quite routinely, to centre our strength ready for if and when the pace hots up again. Just as childbirth is portrayed as a sudden clutching of the stomach, followed by a few shrieks and then a thin cry from behind a closed door, cancer is shown as a stricken face in the doctor's office, followed by brave smiles at the bedside and the cue for violins. It ain't necessarily so.

There is also a stream of constantly changing theories about what causes cancer, about the 'cancer personality' and about cancer-inducing aspects of our lifestyle. As with the statistics relating to survival rates, medical research regurgitated as newspaper headlines causes anxiety without foundation. Most of the theories have no wide medical acceptance, and can often do severe damage by actual misrepresentation; for example in the claims that the alternative therapies of Bristol Centre regimes were actually making people sicker. The claims were statistically flawed and numerically insignificant; they just weren't true, but they did enormous damage to the fragile and vital trust of the Centre's patients, and to its image in the minds of people who might have been helped there.

I also saw a misleading advertisement in the British press which stirred me into action. Claiming that dietary changes could substantially decrease a family's risk of developing cancer in the future, this organisation offered to sell you an expensive diet book which turned out to be based on the familiar and unremarkable principles of high fibre and low fat – information which is probably available in any library which keeps Health Educational Authority literature. I complained about these adverts to the various newspapers which carried them and one of them instituted its own investigation into the organisation behind the claims. This revealed that similar complaints in America concerning this organisation had resulted in its being investigated and criticised for failing to use a satisfactory percentage of its income for the research it claimed to be funding. The newspaper was sufficiently disturbed by these discoveries to drop further advertising – at substantial financial loss. Since then, I have not seen any more advertising by this organisation in any other newspapers.

As I see it, most washing powders work reasonably well; less fat and more fibre in our diets will improve our general health. But just as you probably don't believe that any one washing powder is as good as the adverts claim, don't let anyone persuade you that any expensive diet book, fruit kernel wonder pill or any other miracle cure is going to guarantee that it will make you safe from cancer.

What I felt then, and still feel very strongly, is that having cancer is not my fault. It is not your fault. It is not a punishment for some unknown crime in our past. I did not deserve to get cancer, and neither did you. Whether we consumed additives by the bucketful in our youth, whether we internalised our stress to the point where we twanged with tension like a violin, we didn't deserve this.

But it seems that, in the absence of definite knowledge, we have to develop theories to explain why we don't have absolute control of our lives. Of course serious research must be done into dietary and environmental patterns in the incidence of cancer. But the logical conclusion of fretting over what might have given you cancer once you've actually got it is like saying, 'Serves you right!' I was told the most extraordinary theories about what might be behind my disease by people who really thought they were being sympathetic. Sometimes it seems that everything you have done, eaten or felt in your whole life has been implicated in one theory or another. Most of these theories seem to vanish without trace as soon as the shock headlines have filled the required amount of space.

My last swipe at the media is, aptly enough, on the matter of obituaries. Even if a cause of death is not normally mentioned, cancer will be, even if victims are in their nineties. It's routinely referred to as 'a long struggle bravely borne'. I always wonder how accurate a picture that is. In my own case it's two and a half years since a definite diagnosis. It hasn't been a ball, but within that time I've been to work, gone on holiday, cleaned the bath – led a normal life in an abnormal situation. Out of those two and a half years, the real times of hell, or 'struggle' as the papers would say, have been just a few weeks. Yet if cancer gets me in the end, five years, ten years down the line, will all those other weeks of peace and pleasure be thought of as of no account? Don't they matter? I know my life is worth more than that; there's more to me than my cancer, and it's not and never could be the most significant thing in my life.

## FEAR OF FAILURE

Some people seem to feel that having cancer is another kind of life test, like making it up the job ladder, or running marathons; that they are required to put on a good performance. But cancer isn't something you can separate from the rest of your life like athletic training or study. It is far more basic and pervasive than that, and it seemed to me that the sooner I could accept that my cancer was not a period to be got through so that I could get back to my old life, the easier it became to see the new rules, the new goals of this new life: to slow down, to see the value in small achievements, almost as if I were now opening my eyes wider to take in new, brighter colours and shapes. And the colours and shapes were important in themselves, not just the background scenery.

For example, I live on the edge of a common, which I have always valued. Before I had cancer, the common was just a pleasant way to walk to the pub, or to quiet a fractious baby. When I was very ill, I measured out my slowly returning strength by walking from tree to tree, trying for one more each day. I realised that there were whole paths, whole areas I'd never explored, never even knowing they were there as I'd crossed the common backwards and forwards on the same well-worn tracks. Now that I'm well, I know every inch of it, but it's still different every day, and I don't miss a thing – all the colour, all the animal tracks, and all the pleasure of being able to walk for as long and as often as I want.

Living in the present can be a hard lesson to learn. You

may be going through a huge range of emotions and feel as if your fears are out of control. But this may just be the way you are beginning to deal with cancer *now*, and nobody has the right to suggest that you are weak or negative, or that you are making things worse for yourself, or that any set of dietary rules, positive thinking mantras or religious orthodoxy could change everything if only you could be strong enough to follow all the rules. But while your feelings are entirely normal and even therapeutic, there is a difference between *experiencing* all these emotions and *feeding* them, going back to them over and over again, and not allowing yourself to move onwards. Regretting the past or denying the present, getting stuck in anger at what's happened, can all undermine your efforts in the here and now.

It's not better than what I used to do; the pleasure I get from being able to walk long distances doesn't make up for what I've lost, but it has a value of its own, and for much of the time that's enough. The rage I felt when I was told I had cancer, the anger at the pain and damage it did to my life, these emotions have had their time, and can no longer take me any further forward. Acceptance, neither grudging nor conditional, of the way things are now, brings its own peace.

I decided long ago that if cancer is going to get me in the end, I would be really furious if I'd wasted all the time I had left waiting for it to strike. And if it never comes back, the same thing applies. It doesn't work all the time; I still get angry and I still get scared now and then. But as long as cancer cannot paralyse my life to the exclusion of all else, I am not beaten.

This may sound like Winston Churchill and his, 'All I can offer you is blood, sweat, and tears . . .' But nothing I or anyone else can say is going to suddenly make everything fall into place and make sense to you. None of the tricks I am going to suggest will work all the time. Probably you'll find your own ways to side-step, ignore, or muddle through your black days. But in the end you can do it, you can take back your life. There is always hope, even if you can't see it for yourself. You just have to give yourself a chance, maybe more than one, to move beyond the emotional pain to being in charge of your life again.


## FEAR OF DYING

> *Nor dread nor hope attend*
> *A dying animal:*
> *A man awaits his end*
> *Dreading and hoping all;*
> *. . . Man has created death.*
> W B Yeats


For many of us, finding out we've got cancer is the first time we really have to consider our own mortality. We know in theory that one day we will die, but we don't get any practice in accepting the natural cycle of birth and death because we live so far from nature. It seems ironic in a society that is constantly exposed to real and fictional images of death and destruction, that our own death is still a taboo subject.

None of that helps at all, of course, when you are actually confronted for the first time with a life-threatening illness. But again, give yourself time. As with the fear of the disease itself, the fear of death recedes once you are within the 'system' of cancer, and not looking at it from the outside. As treatment progresses, and if you can allow yourself to take each step at a time, the business of the moment takes over. Try to focus on any small step which shows that you are making progress – instead of seeing the process as a whole and feeling swamped by how far there still may be to go, with death waiting at the end of the road.

I don't remember that I worried very much about my own death except as it would affect my family. If death is the end, there was no need to worry. If there is an after-life, I didn't think I'd done anything very terrible in my life (and which number of the seven deadly sins is pride?). Maybe I just don't have enough imagination, but the fact of death was not high on my top ten terrors. What did worry me was being in pain, or going on too long in a helpless state. I'd read accounts of bargains struck between couples that in such a case one partner would help the other to die, but when faced with the cold reality I could only think of what an intolerable burden it would be on anyone to live with the responsibility of another's death. My experience in intensive care after my third operation also made me wonder how I'd know when there really was no point in going on any longer, because I felt so hopeless while I was there and now I know I just needed more time.

All I can say is that once I was inside the process of treatment, the idea of death receded and was simply not a priority issue any more. When I was powerless to change a situation, I tried to work at helping myself to live with it, rather than breaking my heart about what was outside my control.

Although I was not a regular church-goer, I was brought up in a religion. Whether it was because of childhood memories, or the need to hand over the burden of my illness to a perceived outside force, I found a great deal of comfort just sitting in our local church. The vicar and his wife are very much a part of the local community so I already knew them, from nursery school and boys' clubs and just from around the village, which made the church feel even more like a possible refuge. I suppose it felt like surrendering all responsibility for my life, which gave me a kind of breathing space. Yet to sit in an empty church is very peaceful, even if one's religious faith isn't certain.

I also felt supported by the number of people who told me quite simply that they were praying for me. It was warming to know that just about every religious faith had somebody who was on my side, as if I was somehow hedging my bets! I had Protestants and Catholics, Baptists and Methodists, Jews and Muslims, Hindus and Buddhists – all keeping me on their lists. How could I fail?

# 10

# Your Family
# And Other Liabilities

*Almost all our relationships begin, and most of them continue
as forms of mutual exploitation, a mental or physical barter,
to be terminated when one or both parties run out of goods.*
                                                          W H Auden


The first time I read the quote at the start of this chapter, when I was still at school, I thought what a mean and cynical view it showed, and I've always thought so. But what's happened in the last couple of years has made me accept that perhaps the old misery knew a thing or two. And boy, did I run out of goods!

Of course I know that there are individuals who find that the experience of cancer was productive for them. There must be, because I kept reading about the new enlightenment people found, about the benefits of a challenge met and overcome, and about the new insights into one's relationships. I even read that cancer gave many people their first real freedom in life – the view of a popular psychiatrist who might benefit from an extended spell in his own Radio Chair. Well, I'm afraid I didn't find the two years I spent battling against cancer positive in any way, least of all in my relationships with other people.

Maybe I just don't know the kind of people who thrive on pressure, and become heroic in adversity. I'm quite certain that I'm not one myself. There was a much vaunted saying in the Eighties: 'When the going gets tough, the tough get going.' For this cancer patient at least, when the going got tough, sometimes I just about held myself together, but I was just as likely to fall apart and pull the bedclothes over my head . . .

In fact, I found the opposite was true. My cancer was just as destructive of my personal relationships as of my health and my peace of mind. Although the damage wasn't permanent, it is not forgotten, but one thing I'm sure of: it didn't bring out the best in any of us.

I've never been a fan of the Jane Eyre school of moral strength gained through suffering. My life before cancer was happy and secure, and none of the miseries I went through made me suddenly realise with a blinding flash what life was all about. Cancer showed me things about myself and other people that I would have been far happier not knowing. My relationships with quite close friends have been irrevocably altered by their reactions to my illness. I am angered and hurt by remarks made, meetings avoided, long silences from people who could not cope with the fact of my pain and need, although they had come to me in the past with crises of their own. The isolation we felt, on the one hand from our contemporaries who had their own responsibilities and priorities, and on the other from our families who needed *us* to support *them*, was at first very frightening.

Your friends and family can't really win, of course. Getting the right balance in sympathy and support is a pretty impossible task. You may be feeling strong and determined one day, and be irritated by overt sympathy. You may want to wallow in angst another day, and feel bereft when people are brisk rather than cosseting.

Once again, I found that cancer has its own rules. Some people who were good friends hardly came near me when I was ill, as if it were a form of plague with risk of contagion. Some came at first, but became swamped by the situation as it worsened and lengthened. Others whom I would not immediately have thought of as close gave constant and enormous support when it came to the crunch. Once you can accept that living with cancer is a totally abnormal situation, outside the bounds of all normal social rules, you can accept that many people will almost certainly let you down. And you can forgive them too, when instead of asking you how *you* feel about your cancer, they tell you how terrible *they* feel about it. You can learn to accept that it's human nature to feel, 'Thank God it's not happening to me,' rather than feel betrayed by those who will only ever see *your* cancer in terms of how it affects *them*. You can forgive those who simply cannot handle pain in those they love, and who therefore desert you until such time as you can once again be the person they knew.

Much will also depend on what your role has been in the past in relation to those close to you. If you've always been 'the strong one', you may find people will continue to rely on you to take the initiative, even to support them through what they see as a crisis for themselves – and as a crisis of your making! If you've never needed emotional support, this new experience may floor them. You are changing the ground rules of the relationship and it may just not be possible for them to support you, no matter how often they've relied on you in the past.

Your own nature is also relevant, of course. I've always been independent, and it took me a long time to realise that I'd always seen asking for support as a sign of weakness, as some kind of failure on my part. Now I had to come to terms with the fact that I had no choice but to ask for help in lots of different ways. The failure of so many people close to me to provide this help, even when asked, and in fact the extent to which they added to the strain, was in fact only part of the hardest realisation of all. From the moment I became sure I was seriously ill, I had to learn to accept that I could never again be the person my friends and relations had once known. So the cancer was a process, if you like, that led me away from the person I used to be, through all the treatment and its pressures, and is still going on. And there was absolutely no choice about that either.

So forget the normal rules of putting others first, being

unselfish, shielding others from the negative sides of your nature. This is a serious fight; you need to concentrate on yourself, on your needs, and on your feelings. You have more than enough to deal with, without trying to see anybody else's point of view. There will be time for mending fences later.

This sounds hard and selfish, I know, but I really believe that the needs of others can, if you let them, drain your vital energy at the time you can least afford it. You will obviously be concerned about the impact your cancer and its treatment will have on the people you love, but beware that their feelings don't make you start feeling guilty and miserable simply because of what you feel you're putting them through. The logical conclusion of that kind of thinking is that you end up apologising for making them feel so bad, which is both destructive and self-perpetuating. What are you going to do – end up regretting that you were ever born because you've ended up causing heartache to others? There are going to be enough causes for misery without looking round for more.

I'm not trying to pass judgement on any of the types of reaction you may meet – only to identify the kind of people who cannot help you and will probably just add to your problems. It doesn't mean you'll never be able to forgive them, that you won't love them or be close to them any more, but they can't help right at this minute and will almost certainly do positive harm to your morale.

Cancer is a very isolating disease, and people who patently fail to understand what you're going through and what you need from them will only make you feel even more detached from the rest of the human race.

Here are what I found were the common types, and how to deal with them, at least in part.

## NEAREST AND DEAREST

First of all come the wailers, likely to be immediate family and close friends. They will cry, or turn away to hide their tears, every time they see you. They will look at you sadly so that you feel you have at most only days to go before you inevitably die. If you talk about your treatment, they will smile sadly as if they are glad you are able to fool yourself, but of course they know there's no hope really. I found this wallowing in misery, this inability to feel any optimism even for my sake, incredibly draining and in the end infuriating. The only real solution we found was to keep the wailers entirely away from us until each crisis was over. While my life and everything dear to me was under such enormous threat, I had no room for sympathy or understanding for those who gave up at the first hurdle.

This probably sounds unkind and exaggerated, and although I hope you're spared this kind of reaction, I'm afraid I doubt it. If you feel reluctant to be harsh with these people, try looking at it this way. They are turning your agony into drama about themselves; their motives at base are actually selfish. So, if people can only tell you how bad *they* feel about *your* cancer, keep them away. Let them carry their own emotional baggage while you're busy pushing that rock up the mountain. How's that for mixed metaphors?

Then there are the hearties, also likely to be people whom under normal circumstances you are reasonably close to. They cannot cope with the reality of a life-threatening illness, and have little imagination to give them any insight into what you're suffering. So they refuse to acknowledge your fears; they are embarrassed by evidence of your distress; their eyes slide away and they leave as soon as possible. They are recognisable by such phrases as, 'Oh come on now,' and 'You mustn't think like that.'

Trying to talk about your fears, trying to acknowledge your terror of the illness, the future, what it's doing to your children, to someone you think loves you but who is clearly trying to shut you up as fast as possible is a tremendously destructive and lonely feeling. You feel as though you're somehow cut off from the rules of the game, you've dropped out of society. You have no right to voice your pain because it's somehow in bad taste, or embarrassing. However good a friend you are in ordinary circumstances, this level of need is unreasonable and unacceptable.

93

## FRIENDS AND ACQUAINTANCES

A less intrusive but still hurtful category are the avoiders. People who, when they hear about your illness, will simply drop out of sight as if you've suddenly become unclean. If you meet them and they can't avoid it, they will chat feverishly about something else, then ask nervously, 'How are you?' in tones that show they're terrified you might tell them.

The theorists are my pet hate. They will assume that your illness and cancer in general are the only subjects you can possibly be interested in discussing, and will buttonhole you at social gatherings to dispense their wisdom. If I had a fiver for every time I've been told, as if being given a rare gift of deep insight, 'Of course, state of mind is the important thing,' or 'I think it's something that's in all of us,' I could have bought my own CT scanner. Try asking, in the sweetest tone you can muster, 'How do you come to know so much about it?' They will also have an inexhaustible source of case histories (which they also believe you'll naturally be fascinated by) of friends of friends of friends who had the disease, usually totally unrelated to your own experience and at some point in the past when treatment was at a far less developed level than at present. Refrain from the very understandable impulse to punch them in the eye; engage in your favourite relaxation technique or, if symptoms allow, have another drink.

But among all these, we also found that the most tremendous practical help and support came from people we'd least expected it from. Friends we'd met through the children overwhelmed us with the generosity of their time and effort, giving us precious time in which to rest and recover. The children were ferried to and from school, taken on outings in the holidays, in fact virtually adopted by these lovely women without fuss or hesitation. Because they gave me the chance to delegate many of the physical tasks of an ordinary day, I was able to concentrate on being delighted to see the children when they came home from school, instead of being exhausted by dealing with their basic needs. When I had radiotherapy, a group of women I knew got together with my father-in-law and briskly drew up a rota to take me backwards and forwards, which was another enormous pressure removed.

Tiredness, as I have often said, is the great enemy, and given what your body and mind are going through it's all too easy to add to your problems with the effects of exhaustion. However independent a person you are, do try to let others do whatever they can to help. People want very much to show they care by practical measures. Let them do your shopping, entertain your children, cook your meals, tidy the garden or whatever.

But also remember that people will, without any selfish intention, take you at your word and deed. If you insist on struggling to make coffee for visitors and then feel lousy for hours afterwards, that's your fault – not theirs for failing to be sensitive to your state of body and mind. If you feel drained by too many visitors, that's your fault for not telling them that it's time for your nap now. Resist the temptation to say, 'No thanks' to offers because you feel reluctant to be beholden or worry that you're exploiting people. I found people were only too delighted to be told, 'Yes please, that would be such a help.' People don't know what to say or do for you. So tell them that you'd love an apple pie, a load of washing done and ironed, a drive out to the shops. I certainly wish I'd taken more advantage of the offers I received, and feel now that I probably hurt some feelings by trying (and failing) to remain self-sufficient.

## PARTNERS

If you're lucky, there will be someone very close to you who will share this journey fully with you. That person – partner, parent or child – will be under the most enormous strain. To watch somebody you love go through hell is to be in hell yourself. In fact, I've often thought that it can be much worse for the one who watches and worries than it is for the one at the sharp end.

As well as the emotional pressure, the partner is often faced with enormous practical difficulties. Keeping people informed, domestic needs, visiting the hospital, often coupled with trying to continue working, all adds up to a nightmarish schedule, while you're sitting up expectantly in hospital waiting once more to be entertained and told how marvellous you're being. And while attention is focused on you, there's often little comfort or emotional support offered to the partner.

They are expected, often for extended periods of time, to be entirely unselfish, utterly devoted, a tower of strength and understanding, and quite oblivious of their own needs. If they're tired, have a headache or a cold, there's no one to sympathise – because of course it's nothing compared to what's happening to you and how could they possibly complain? If they feel like staying at home and going to bed instead of turning up every day at visiting time, they will probably suffer paroxysms of guilt that they should even dream of putting their own needs first. If they feel irritated to screaming point by the extra demands on them, or resentful at the way life is treating them, or just plain cheesed off with the whole depressing business, they still have to show up smiling for you to lean on and moan at.

Another assumption that seems to be made is that couples or families will draw closer together when faced with a crisis like cancer. For heaven's sake don't pillory yourself if this isn't your experience. I asked a lot of other patients for their opinions on this one, because I wondered if I was being overly cynical in feeling that this is another of the myths beloved of those who have nothing more constructive to say. Nobody I met or heard from felt it had happened to them. When I had suggested earlier to my husband that perhaps we had jettisoned some of the trivial points of contention in our marriage because of what we had gone through together, and so become closer, he told me in no uncertain terms not to *dare* to make up some sort of soppy postscript just to kid ourselves that all the pain and exhaustion of the past years hadn't been entirely in vain. So it was fairly clear what *he* thought!

The only thing to have come out of my cancer is that I have survived; that I am now living my life, and my family still has a wife and mother. I have been luckier than many. End of story.

So I can't see how people reach new closeness through suffering; in fact, I believe that for many it's the opposite.

There are so many new emotions to deal with. Most people will never have considered to any extent the death of their partner. Once that possibility becomes a real threat, it can make people start to withdraw, to begin to act almost as if that absolute separation had already taken place and they were starting to get used to it. This act of self-protection can cause the patient to feel there is not enough sympathy, not enough listening, which brings resentment on the one hand and guilt on the other for the heavy demands being made. Or partners or families can struggle to act as if everything is normal, which they think is the best way to approach the problem but which makes the cancer patient feel like the loneliest person on earth.

This enormous stress, which can continue unrelieved for weeks or even longer, proves too much for some, and who can really blame them? I'm only surprised that so many of us seem to get through in the end. I heard stories of partners who simply couldn't stand the pain any more, and stayed away for a while or for ever. I heard that some patients couldn't stand the responsibility, as they saw it, of causing such pain, and asked not to be visited in hospital or questioned about treatment. Some patients, having finished treatment, made enormous changes in their lives, as if their cancer had been the catalyst for a whole new direction, leaving their families, their careers and their past behind them, as if only by escaping everything could they escape their cancer experience.

We just wanted to be ourselves again in our normal life together. My husband came to see me in hospital every day, although he was sometimes so tired that I get choked up remembering it. Often we didn't talk much, just taking strength from each other, although I know who was doing most of the taking! Sometimes I'd be calm and confident, eager to hear news of the children and with news of some progress I'd felt in the day; sometimes it was hard to find anything bright to say. I remember one night in intensive care, when I felt so bad with the tube in my nose and my oxygen mask, still having enough vanity to feel totally uncharacteristic bitter and poisonous jealousy of the pretty nurse who was answering his questions because I could hardly talk myself!

But I don't feel, and never have, that we drew any closer together, nor that any such closeness could ever make up for the worry I saw, and sometimes still see, in his face. He is a private man, and because I respect that, I feel his presence in this book doesn't begin to do him justice. But I didn't need to see him suffer so much to know his worth. And when I asked my friends if they saw any gain in their relationships as a result of sharing their own cancer experience, the answer was the same. It costs so much more than it brings, and all you can hope is that the price is not too high.

I don't want to make it seem as though relationship problems are inevitable, or permanently scarring, but I think it is so important to be realistic with each other. And I know of one woman who, having faced a crisis much worse than having cancer (the death of one of her children), said how terribly relieved she was to hear us say these things. She and her husband had experienced terrible problems communicating with each other about their loss, and she was deeply comforted to know that others had also not experienced the mythical rose-coloured happy ending. Her message alone made me feel it was worth saying that all may not be sweetness and light.

# 11

# Relaxation, Focusing And Negative Thinking

Cancer is frightening, demoralising, depressing, but mostly it is exhausting. Tiredness is the constant, from the early symptoms, through surgery and convalescence; it is particularly evident during and briefly after secondary treatment like chemotherapy and radiotherapy. You are likely to be physically tired from the treatment, and mentally tired from the enormous pressure you're under. And the worst part of all this tiredness is that unless you give in to it, unless you learn to pace yourself and learn to relax, then feelings of lowness and depression are inevitable. And when you're tired, you're in no position to tell yourself that the reason you're depressed is that you're tired! It's a vicious circle, but one that you can to a certain extent avoid.

Your body is under threat, and you are being forced to fight a continuous series of battles. You will win some, probably lose some; you will pick yourself up and hold yourself together more times than you will believe you can. Day by day, obstacle by obstacle, you can do it. But if (quite understandably) you try to hang on to carrying on as normal with no concessions to your cancer, you are likely to exhaust yourself.

This is not a test. Nobody is going to be giving marks for bravery, and nobody loves a martyr. Some people, if cancer is detected early and surgery is slight, find that they can go to work while they're having chemotherapy or radiotherapy. Others will be weakened by pre-treatment symptoms and find they need a long convalescence. You must listen to what your body is telling you and go along with it, so that you get enough rest to allow you to recover.

The ability to relax is a rare gift. In normal life, physical tension is ever-present, even if we're not aware of it, and it is tiring and unproductive. Mental strain is also exhausting, and when you're fighting cancer you cannot afford to waste energy, because you will be confronted by a series of stressful situations. From the tension generated in the waiting-room to full-blown panic, the pressure on your mind and body is immense, and any ways of reducing this pressure will be tremendously helpful to you. It's also a good idea to practise these techniques straightaway before you really need them, as if you're not naturally a restful person it might take you a while to relax into them.

Breathing out as hard as you can will automatically relax your body. Take in a normal breath, hold it for a few seconds and then try to breathe out every bit of air in your lungs. Do it a few times, but don't take great gulps of air or strain when breathing out or you could end up hyperventilating (taking too much oxygen into the body) which will make you feel dizzy. If this does happen, take small breaths in, hold them, then let them out slowly (if you count to six in, hold for six, then out for six you should re-establish a normal rhythm quite quickly).

Lift your shoulders as high as you can, hold for a few seconds, and then let them drop. Screw up your face as hard as you can, hold it, then let go. Let your body drop from the waist and let everything flop. If you lie down on a mat or a towel you can repeat this tensing and releasing action for each part of your body, and it really does work. You might well be surprised by the difference, especially in your shoulders and stomach, if you get into the habit of repeatedly checking to make sure you're not tensing these muscles.

My favourite way of dealing with all sorts of stressful situations is to imagine myself in a favourite place. There is a house with a little terrace where we've spent several very happy holidays, and I imagine myself there, in the sunshine. Perhaps I'm reading a book, or I've got a glass of wine, or sometimes

I change the flowers in the pots for a bit of variety! I concentrate on the physical sensations of sitting in the chair, of the sun on my skin, the details of the view, the bird-song, the sound of the breeze etc, etc. I'm sure it sounds a bit daft, but the more I used this distraction, the easier it became to drop into, and the more effective it was for me. I've used it to have a drain taken out of an operation site, to help me through bad days in hospital, even to have a tube put into my nose and down my throat. And it really works. In fact, the last time I had a body scan the operator had to call my name three times before I 'came back' and answered him. But it does need concentration. It's not just a matter of thinking nice thoughts, but of closing your eyes, letting your mind take over and removing yourself completely from the here and now.

A variation on this theme that I've used quite a lot is a favourite walk. You need to know the walk very well, so that you can concentrate on each step; the changing view; the leaves, earth or the pavement under your feet. Or you can mentally plant out a garden border, or paint a wall, or swim in the sea. Any situation in which you're happy and relaxed will work, and the more you let your imagination run free, the more effective it will be in distancing you from whatever nastiness you're trying to shut out.

Another good way I found of taking back charge of my mind which has become a favourite of mine, if not of my neighbours, is to get into a very hot bath and sing at the top of my voice. Aesthetic niceties should be sacrificed absolutely; the louder you sing, the better because the sheer volume means it's physically impossible to worry at the same time! Marching songs, Buddy Holly or even nursery rhymes work very well, and not only will you be unable to worry but the sheer idiocy of the whole business will hopefully cheer you up in the process. I specialise in all the arias from *Tosca* (soprano, tenor *and* baritone) and early Beatles, with the occasional Shirley Bassey, but that can be awkward because of the gestures.

If you are physically able to do it, I found that walking quite briskly, talking to myself in an authoritative voice in the manner of an American tennis player is also a good morale raiser and tension banisher. Telling yourself in a continuous undertone that you're doing great, you keep it up now, nobody can beat you kid, and so and so on can do a good job of psyching you up, especially when combined with the physical speeding-up produced by the walking. I did find that other pedestrians tended to cross the road to avoid me, but the benefits were worth it.

Focusing your mind on your priorities will also save you energy and concentrate your forces where they're most required. Nobody can banish negative thinking entirely, but it's a waste of time and very demoralising. So if your mind is continually running along the lines of *Why me? What did I do to deserve this? How long have I got?* then it may be you could make use of counselling to break the cycle. Everybody has these kinds of thoughts; we wouldn't be human if we didn't. It's absolutely understandable, but it gets in the way of any progress, and it's terribly wearing to continue feeling helpless in the face of what you see as overwhelming odds.

Unfortunately, you can't wait for medical staff to notice your need; it will be up to you to ask for it and maybe to keep on asking. As I found to my cost, it's possible to leave it so long that the end result is far worse than taking early and decisive action. Maybe all you need is to talk through your fears to cut them down to size; maybe you want some more specialised help, but the sooner you ask, the quicker you will be able to cut through the period of adjustment and concentrate on getting through to the other side of your cancer.

Once we have brought under control the first feelings of shock, disbelief, anger, denial and all the other reactions we feel on first finding out we have cancer, the going gets a lot easier. Once you are within the business of treatment – turning up for appointments, waiting to see doctors – taking each hurdle as it comes becomes much simpler, and the enormous questions of life and death fade a little into the background. It becomes easier to follow the idea that Small is Beautiful. Any gain, however small, should be grounds for self-congratulation. The body's capacity for recovery is immense, and you should be able to note any visible improvement as you recover from an operation, or count off each day of chemotherapy, or each blast of radiotherapy, towards the day when it will be over. It won't always be that easy; you'll get fed up, miserable, frustrated and worn out. But those days too will pass and you can start again. And if you are physically as relaxed (and therefore, prepared) as you can be, then keeping up your spirits even when the going gets tough takes less energy.

# 12

# In The Hands Of The Experts

*Whoever gives an invalid advice acquires a feeling of superiority over him, whether the advice is taken or rejected. For this reason susceptible and proud invalids hate their advisers even more than their illness.*

Friedrich Wilhelm Nietzsche

## DOCTORS

Doctors are probably the prime example of the 'no-win' profession. If they're telling people bad news, it's very hard not to think of them as somehow responsible. And heaven help them if one word could be construed as insensitive or patronising. With a disease like cancer, they don't even have professional omniscience to comfort them, because there are simply no definitive, cut and dried, absolute answers. I always had the feeling during hospital appointments that if I could only find the right form of words to ask the same question and ask it often enough, eventually somebody would say to me, 'Yes, now you're fine and nothing bad will ever happen to you again.' But they never did because they never can, and however comforting it might be to blame them, it's not their fault.

Because of my experiences at the hands of GPs, I would always advise anybody who feels there is something wrong with their body, but is getting no satisfactory explanation, to keep on trying to get more second opinions until they're happy the matter is proven. It still frightens me that if I had been less bolshy, and had allowed myself to be convinced that anxiety was my only problem, I would probably have died. As it is, although there is absolutely no point in pursuing the matter, I am reasonably convinced that if I'd been listened to from the first, I would not have developed secondary cancer.

On the other hand, because of the huge advances in medicine and in medical technology, as well as TV programmes that thrive on images of the doctor as infallible saviour, we tend to expect miracles as routine. But many doctors badly need to take an intensive course in public relations, to undo the truth of the old joke, 'What's the difference between God and a doctor? God doesn't think he's a doctor.' Or a quote I read somewhere: 'Why does my doctor act as if he's removed my brain along with my gall-bladder?'

There has been quite a lot of discussion about the need to include interpersonal skills, as the jargon goes, in the medical school syllabus, but you're probably not going to benefit in the near future. However, I think it's important not to see your doctors as the enemy. It can't be very easy telling people they've got cancer and all that it entails, and so perhaps it is not too surprising that so many of them do it rather badly. There's also the very understandable reaction of patients transferring emotion away from its real source. So if you're being told something dreadful, it can be easier to get angry at the doctor's arrogance or brusque manner than to face the real matter at hand, which is your illness. In the end, does it really matter how beautiful your doctor's manners are, as long as he knows what he's doing? Which isn't to say that a good bitch about the arrogant so-and-so won't do you the world of good, as long as it doesn't sap your energy or make you lose confidence in the medical treatment he's dishing out.

I was very lucky on the whole with the doctors I saw, once I was actually able to convince somebody that I was sick. Even so, I felt that whenever I had appointments, my anxiety about the outcome meant that I found it hard to absorb all of what was being said to me. Details of what was to happen would

go out of my head. Afterwards, when it was too late, I'd have
questions either that I'd prepared beforehand, or that had
come out of what was said – but nobody to ask. The best
solution I found was that after my first operation, my husband
would always come with me, and between us we could make
up the whole picture of what we'd been told. I would also
make a written list of what we wanted to know so that things
didn't get forgotten. Taking notes at the time might be useful
if you don't have a companion; I even heard one radio discussion that advised tape-recording the appointment to
remember, or go over, what was discussed.

I always found it hard to remember and accept that with
the best will in the world, most hospital doctors are under
great pressure of time, and their treatment priorities have to
be physical rather than emotional. Your doctor is unlikely to
be able to go into very much detail about your fears and
worries, however sympathetic s/he may be. S/he will also want
to be reassuring about the outcome, which may appear brisk
and uncaring. I found it useful to try to look at it from the
other side; they were being straightforward and no-nonsense
because they knew they could do something to help; not
because they were insensitive to their patients' needs and
fears.

I was well aware I was not the sort of person who would
want to challenge or reject the treatment I was being
offered, or who would choose to explore other options. But
the doctors I met were certainly not dismissive of alternative
therapies, and in fact many hospitals encourage the use of
complementary techniques like aromatherapy or reflexology.
Again, I feel it's important not to treat the doctor as the enemy,
automatically opposed to any unorthodoxy. If you have strong
feelings about your treatment, you should express them. I
knew one patient who was very reluctant to undergo chemotherapy, and asked if any alternative was available. In that
particular case, it was decided that an alternative could be
substituted, but that isn't always possible as far as conventional
medicine is concerned. For me, the idea of rejecting standard
treatment for other regimes would have required a degree

of self-confidence and conviction that I knew would be impossible.

I, and other patients I know, always felt that we were being told the truth about our condition, even when the news was bad. My husband did feel at times as if bad news was parcelled out in small amounts to make it easier to deal with, but on the whole we were kept informed very well. I soon learned always to ask for an explanation of technical terms I didn't understand, which can be a bit daunting if somebody in an exquisite suit, with an air of supreme confidence, is in full flow; but there is always an intelligible explanation, so why not ask for it? Taking part in discussion will also help you to feel less like another body on the production line.

Another excellent reason for asking for explanations of anything that bothers you is that simple misunderstandings can cause extreme and quite unnecessary stress. I once went through weeks of worry because of just such a misconception. I had asked my surgeon, when I was at a very low ebb physically and mentally after my third operation, whether I was 'going to get out of this in the end'. I hadn't asked such a direct question before, and he thought for a moment before he said, very seriously it seemed, 'There's a chance that you will.' I took those words and his tone to mean that the outlook was pretty bleak, only a chance that I'd make it, and it most certainly added to my stress when my recovery was so painfully slow.

But when, three months later, he seemed to be saying something more optimistic, I repeated my question and reminded him of his previous answer. He was surprised and apologetic that I'd put such a construction on his words, saying that he'd been optimistic that radiotherapy would eradicate any further disease. A *good* chance, in fact.

Another example came at an appointment with the oncologist. After some discussion about progress, she examined me as she'd often done before. Her next words were, 'I think you should have another scan.' I was immediately panic-stricken that she'd found something she felt needed investigation. My husband also felt there was a connection between the examination and the proposal of a further scan. But when we asked, we were reassured that there was no such connection; it was simply that she wanted to keep a regular check on progress. But at least this time we'd asked, instead of worrying for weeks!

It's so easy for patients to think the worst, if a carelessly worded remark is left hanging in the air without clarification. So much depends on what we are being told by our doctors, so much trust is placed in them, that we are weighing up every chance word they say, dissecting every expression and tone, looking for any tell-tale anxiety or reluctance to meet our eyes. Such evidence is just as likely to mean that the doctor's been up most of the night as that there's something terrible nobody's telling you.

If you see a succession of different doctors, it's highly likely that at least one of them is going to irritate the hell out of you. Their manner, the way they ignore you for minutes at a time when you first enter the room, or ask the nurse questions about you that you are perfectly capable of answering for yourself, or always use the 'we' form of address, as in, 'And how are we feeling today?' All are pet hates from different friends' experiences.

The worst example of almost unbelievable insensitivity happened to a friend of mine even after her chief exposure to doctors and their little ways was over. She had gone through surgery for breast cancer, chemotherapy and radiotherapy, and the long haul back to physical well-being. She was delighted when she landed a new job; it seemed to be the start of a whole new beginning after some very bad times. I saw her just after she'd had the medical required for the job, and all that optimism and pleasure had been destroyed. When she had given him her medical history, which was already on record, the doctor performing the medical had said quite callously that he would have to *investigate her prognosis*. She was stunned, and told me that it had brought back all the worry she'd thought was past. She felt that she would never be able to escape the shadow hanging over her life. I think she got some comfort from the outrage expressed by those of us she told.

What did this mean for all our futures? Were we now all second-class citizens, handing over to others the right to assess our chances of making it through two, five, ten years? Nobody else had to sign a declaration that they guaranteed not to get run over by a bus, develop kidney failure, or even not to hate the job and leave within a month. Even if there were any justification for that precaution, which I doubt, the means of expressing it were surely unforgivable in a doctor, or in anyone else for that matter. I can only assume that the oncologist he approached (who treated both of us) shared our outrage and bit him sharply on the leg, because the job was confirmed and my friend is loving it.

At the other end of the scale, I went for one of my regular check-ups and the extremely uncomfortable and highly undignified internal examination that goes with it. My consultant then left the room to check on a blood test result, leaving me to get dressed. He came back in just as I had my trousers half on, apologised, and left again. My husband and I were in fits of laughter at this arbitrary courtesy, and when he came back in once more we said that considering what he'd just been doing to me, and how intimately he knew my insides, such punctiliousness seemed rather unnecessary. He grinned at us and said, 'Ah, but when you're on that examination table, or I'm operating on you, you're my patient and I do what I have to. When I'm talking to you, you are a person and I respect your dignity.' Now that's what I call a doctor. A wonderful man, with enormous skills. And how happy I would be if I never, ever had to see him again!

## NURSES

Nurses are usually referred to as marvellous, and as angels. This is to make up to them for the fact that they are over-worked, underpaid and usually undervalued by doctors and by a surprising number of patients. The majority of them are kind and helpful beyond any call of duty, but their real purpose and first priority is to be skilled. So their treatment of you and any advice they give you has a lot of weight behind it, and it's a pity that so many of us treat them as glorified waitresses. Your nurse may well make you a cup of tea in the middle of the night because she's a nice person, but that's not what she's there for.

So try not to get irritated when they take your temperature, or your blood pressure, or ask for any kind of sample, for what feels like the hundredth time that day. These tests are the best and quickest indicators that recovery is progressing as it should. Nurses will be well aware of the kinds of worries you have when you come into hospital with cancer, and are usually able to help in answering questions and passing on information, so don't feel you always have to wait to question the doctor. The nurses are the ones watching your progress as each day passes; they are the experts in this part of your cancer care, so trust them to do their job.

Nurses also come in for more than their fair share of transferred anger and frustration, so try to remember that it's not their fault if, as will undoubtedly happen from time to time: the consultant is hours late on his/her round *again*; your meal was horrible and cold; you slept badly or allowed too many visitors to tire you out, and are just feeling cross.

You can help your nurses by telling them straightaway of any symptom or problem that is worrying you, however trivial it might seem. One thought that should be banished from your head is, 'I don't want to bother anyone . . .' On the reverse side, try to go along with whatever procedure they require, however unnecessary you may think it is. For example, if they want you to go for an X-ray in a wheelchair – do it. Don't insist you can walk perfectly well, then feel dizzy and sick because you can't stand up for that long, and feel lousy for hours afterwards just because you wanted to be independent. And yes, I did.

So do what you can for yourself, but go along with the ward routine – you'll only waste energy if you kick against the system, however ridiculous bits of it may seem. But if any of you discover a satisfactory explanation as to why nurses are so obsessed with the state of your bed – making it, and remaking it – I'd love to hear it.

Oh, and don't buy them chocolates because they have lockers full – a bottle of wine goes down well instead, and after dealing with you and me and dozens more of us all day, they deserve a drink.

# 13

# Going Into Hospital: Before, During And After

## BEFORE YOU GO

If you are normally in charge of running your household, arrange if you can for someone to come in to clean your house. If you are having major surgery, you won't physically be able to do it for a considerable time, and it's miserable if the place looks a mess while you're trying to recuperate. The temptation will be to do it yourself, or feel bad because it's not getting done – both to be avoided. To have everything done thoroughly once a week takes the pressure off.

Again, if you are normally in charge of meals, fill the freezer with convenience foods, especially one-meal-size dishes for yourself. Cooking will be beyond you for a while, and the chances are you won't bother. If you don't eat well, this will not help the recovery process. Get in as many sauces, tins of fish and meat, and salad dressings as you can think of to fill baked potatoes – easy, good food value, cheap – and everybody else in the family can eat them too.

Get yourself some convalescence treats – a special book or record you've always wanted, ritzy bath essence or your favourite malt whisky, nice writing paper or a supply of crosswords. Anything you normally regard as a luxury is good for your morale.

Although I'd always sworn I hated the things, and turn into a gibbering wreck when confronted with one at the other end of the line, I was given an answering machine as a present when I came out of hospital and it was wonderful. People will want to know how you are, but it can be very tiring to be answering the phone and telling the same story over and over again. Putting on an answerphone for a couple of hours, with perhaps a 'progress report' as a message, will let people show their concern without wearing you out. I'm sure it sounds highly anti-social but when you come out of hospital, you will really need to pace yourself and do what you want to do – not be continually going backwards and forwards to answer the phone.

If you think that's going too far, make a list of people to be phoned with news of your progress, for *someone else* to do the ringing! The five people phoned can then each phone five others and so on, so that you don't need to feel like a long-playing record, nobody gets offended and you don't feel guilty.

Consider getting in touch with BACUP (see p. 133) or CancerLink (see p. 134) to establish what help is available in your area. It will be easier to do it now than when you come out, especially if your nearest group is some distance away and you need to arrange for possible home visits.

Although it will be the last thing on your mind, try to make sure all bills and payments are up to date. You don't want to be worried with ugly letters from the bank when you're feeling vulnerable.

Buy or borrow a personal stereo if you don't already have one. Prepare a selection of tapes and a stock of batteries. Music will help you to relax, cut you off from noisy wards, and you can pretend to be asleep more successfully. Story cassettes are good value when you can't be bothered to read, and most big libraries have a good selection. Take one large, easy to read paperback (hardbacks are too heavy for reading lying down). You probably won't need more than one for the first few days as the after-effects of the anaesthetic will probably mean you can read the same chapter four times without being any the wiser.

A cheap plastic plant mister, filled with water, is very refreshing to spray a fine mist on the face in overhot hospitals.

You may need to drink a good deal after the operation, so a bottle of nice squash is a good idea, but do check with the nurses before you start on it.

## LIVING IN HOSPITAL

Hospital life can be frustrating and difficult to adjust to. You may find your own ways of coping, and of making the hospital routine work for you, rather than against you.

When you are admitted to hospital, be prepared. You may have to wait around for hours before anything happens. Take your reading matter, crosswords, knitting, scrabble, and if possible a personal stereo – for the reasons I give above. But even with all this equipment, I still hope you are first on the operating list.

Try to see some sort of progress in each day, even if it is only in adding a few steps to your walk round the hospital corridors. Perhaps one day you'll get rid of a catheter, or the drip will come down and you'll be more mobile. One day you'll only feel able to eat a few mouthfuls; the next day you can manage more. You may be able to take a bath, or read a magazine more than a line at a time. Seeing the promise in these small steps, rather than giving in to the (admittedly enormous) frustration of hospital life, focuses your mind forward, and helps to get over the destructive feelings of helplessness and loss of control that plague cancer patients.

If you become infuriated with the ward orderly who always starts the floor polisher just as you've dropped off to sleep, realise that you're tired and worried and try some relaxation techniques rather than get worked up about the ward routine, which no force on earth has been known to change for the benefit of patients. When you're woken and brought a cup of tea at six o'clock in the morning, then left completely alone for the next two hours, plug yourself into some music to enjoy the peace for a while, or use the chance to grab the bathroom at the one time in the day when it will almost certainly be empty. Trying to roll with the punches of what you can't change will save you energy; irritation, however justified, will get in the way of your progress when there will be enough problems to bring you down without your getting side-tracked by minor irritants. But you can certainly be forgiven for thinking that some of the daily routines have been invented by a malevolent power for maximum winding-up of patients at all times.

Get the nurses on your side about visitors. Arrange a signal that means, 'Help! Get me out of this!' for use when it's all getting too much. I have actually taken a holy vow that unless given a written request to do so, I will never visit anyone in hospital ever again, but that's my own prejudice – you may be delighted to see your nearest and dearest. Nevertheless, it's amazing how thoughtless some people can be in what they say at the bedside, and in how long they stay there. One poor woman wrote to me that all her husband ever did when he came to see her was moan about what a rotten time *he* was having! Happily, I think that's an extreme example, but in many cases I found visits tired me very quickly if the burden of conversation was left to me – and everybody can do without the people who sit by the bed just smiling bravely at you as if they're already at the wake. But any ward sister worthy of the name can clear the premises in two minutes flat if you've got your signals worked out in advance.

Ear plugs and a personal stereo can help enormously in cutting out the noise around you, which can reach pretty impressive levels. I found that an hour spent listening to some favourite music, or a story cassette, did wonders when the comings and goings reached fever pitch. You can also pretend to be asleep more convincingly – you never know, if they think you're asleep they might even leave you alone.

However tired you feel, and however boring it gets, once the nurses have got you up for the first time after your operation, make yourself get out of bed at least every couple of hours and move around for a few minutes. Give yourself a daily target, or pretend you're racing at Sandown Park or in the Olympics – anything to keep you going.

## WHEN YOU'RE HOME AGAIN

When you come home from hospital, be prepared to feel a little more vulnerable, a little less recovered, and much more tired than when you were in hospital. This won't last, but it can be demoralising for a while if you feel you're losing ground. Don't give in to the temptation to start doing all sorts of household jobs or going about too much. Pamper yourself a little, and take it easy, even if every fibre in your body is crying out to get back to normal. Anaesthetics take time to clear out of your system. If you've had a lot of surgery, your body needs time to settle down again. You may well have been short of proper sleep in hospital when you needed it most. Your food, though it will probably be infinitely more appetising, perhaps isn't being brought to you on a tray; you might not even be bothering to eat properly (which in these circumstances may well mean more, and more often, than you were previously used to). You will be weak, inevitably, and if you overdo things you run the risk of getting to a point of tiredness that leaves you weepy and distressed. This state takes far longer to recover from than anything you'll have done can possibly be worth. But you'll probably do it anyway, so in that case try to be realistic and accept that it's just a small setback. Watch the afternoon film with your feet up and say in a Southern Belle drawl, 'Tomorrow is Another Day'!

When I was in hospital, and while I was recovering from the physical effects of treatment, I didn't find I worried a great deal about the long-term implications of cancer – in a way fear took a back seat while I was occupied with appointments and tests. But once I was out of the medical regime, once I felt less like a patient, I started to have problems dealing with my fears, especially at night. I was relieved to find that other people felt the same way, but that didn't help too much at three in the morning when I couldn't control my panicking brain enough to let me sleep. If it went on for longer than half an hour, I found the only way to deal with it was to get up and do something else.

Anything will do, a hot drink, a book, or try turning on the all-night TV. You may find that the unbelievable awfulness of the American sitcoms will distract you from your demons. You can make shopping lists, polish things you may never have polished in your life before, clean the bathroom. These and many other tried and tested distractions helped me stop myself spiralling further into panic, and all without disturbing the rest of the family. In the daytime, a short brisk walk usually did the trick – but anything that breaks the train of disturbing thoughts will do. Because although I sometimes found a burst of tears, or an explosion of fury against my fate could clear the air for a while and even bring about peace of mind, I don't think there's anything to be gained in letting the kind of unreasoning, overwhelming and unfocused fear that I mean by panic run its course.

None of these ideas is going to work all the time, and you'll probably find others that suit you better. But if they get across the sense that you *can* take charge of yourself again, however long it takes, that you *can* weather the emotional storms that cancer brings in its wake, then you're halfway there already.

# 14

# Investigations, Treatment, Drugs And Medical Paraphernalia

The techniques and gadgets described here have something in common with going to the dentist: fears conjured by the imagination are usually far worse than the reality. Some of the procedures may be undignified, but are not painful or horrifying. You may have some or all of these tests at various times. Don't worry if you're having a test that no one else seems to be having. Don't worry if you're not having a test that somebody else *is* having! Different doctors prefer different techniques, and some parts of the body are better highlighted by one method than another. And don't worry if any or all of these tests have to be repeated in your case. It may be to test 'before and after': it may be for technical reasons; it does not mean that things are more serious than first considered. Above all, try to see these procedures as positive steps along the road of treatment, not as unpleasant activities dreamed up by doctors to make you uncomfortable. None of them lasts more than an hour or so, most far less, and they're all helping to give you the best diagnosis and treatment. Any method of relaxation you have started using will help to get you through with the least upset and discomfort.

## INVESTIGATIONS

### Blood Tests
You may start to feel like a pin-cushion as you go through your cancer treatment, but your blood is a very good guide to your general health and the function of certain organs. Some cancers even have 'markers' which can be screened by blood tests. You will also have a blood test before surgery to find out your blood group in case you need a transfusion.

### Biopsy
This is a sample of tissue, obtained in various ways, which can be sent for examination to establish whether cancer is present, and what type it is. There are several methods of taking a biopsy, many of which can be done without going into hospital. A biopsy needle may be used to take cells from a lump in deep tissue (probably under anaesthetic), or a sample of urine or sputum may be used, or cells may be aspirated with a needle and syringe. It all depends on where the abnormal area is found.

### X-rays
A routine X-ray can reveal the organs in the body, show if heart and lungs are healthy and so on. It is usually the first step on the road to diagnosis and may be all your doctor needs to find out what he needs to know.

### Ultrasound
This uses sound waves to bounce off your insides and create pictures on a special screen. You will lie on a bed; some gel (to help conduction of the sound waves) will be spread on the area to be scanned, and a sensor will pass backwards and forwards over the area. Precise measurements have to be taken, so the process can take some time, but it's painless – and quite fascinating to see everything moving around inside you. But you probably won't be any the wiser for looking at the pictures,

it needs a trained operator to make sense of the images. The operators always seemed very friendly and reassuring to me, and would often tell me what was going on, but a full report will be made to your doctor even if nothing is said to you at the time.

## Laparoscopy
Fibre optics can now be used to give doctors a good look inside the body at a suspect area without the need for invasive surgery. A small incision is made, and a sort of mini-video camera on a long tube (I'm not kidding) is inserted into the area to be inspected. Certain minor surgical procedures can also be performed in this way. The great advantage is that, although it does require a general anaesthetic, it is over quickly and can give a very accurate diagnosis.

## CT scanner
This is a very sophisticated X-ray machine that takes a series of pictures of 'slices' of your body. The slices, when read by a qualified operator, can detect even very small tumours or small abnormalities in glands, so that early treatment can be given. Repeat scans may be given to see what effect the treatment has had on specific organs or areas. You will be asked not to eat or drink for a specified time before the scan. You will have to lie on a hard bed, which moves through an opening in the centre of the machine as the pictures are taken. This can get a bit uncomfortable, or a bit cold, so you might want to ask for a blanket or, as I always do, keep your socks on! You will have to keep very still as the pictures are taken, but you will be told over a microphone when to hold your breath, and there will probably be a system of lights on the machine as well.

Depending on what area is to be scanned, you may have a special drink of disclosing fluid half an hour beforehand, or an injection of contrasting dye, or an insertion of disclosing fluid into the rectum, or the special prize that I got, which is all of the above, although I never felt any effects from any of them. Women may also have to insert a tampon into the vagina. The purpose of all of these is to make it even clearer on the pictures where the boundaries of your internal organs are, and to make the reading of the pictures even more accurate. Don't, as I found myself doing the first time I had one, listen for the tone of voice of the operator to give away good or bad news as to what they were seeing. The scan needs to be carefully read as a whole before any definite report can be given. Relaxation, especially going away in your mind to a happy place or task, is very good for this scan, as the machine is large and can be a bit intimidating, and the process does take some time, but I always found that the operators were very aware of this and did their best to be reassuring and friendly.

The reading of the scan, and the presentation of the report on it, will take some time to get back to your doctor, so don't be concerned that any delay means there's anything wrong – it's just one more in the endless list of waits.

**Isotope scans**
A small quantity of a radioactive isotope is injected into a vein. Different isotopes are attracted to different organs in the body, and when the target organ is reached you will be asked to lie, stand or sit in front of a special camera which can produce detailed pictures of what's going on inside you. I had them twice to examine kidney function and it was absolutely fascinating. You do feel a bit like a performer in Mission Control, as somebody comes towards you with your injection in a metal box with a yellow and black radioactivity symbol, but to watch my own body at work was riveting! It's also painless; the amount of radioactivity you receive is harmless and you excrete it quickly.

**MR scan**
This uses a magnetic field to build up extremely detailed pictures of the body. There is usually no particular preparation, but you cannot take any metal into the scanner room. The table you lie on moves into the scanning machine, and the whole thing takes about an hour. I haven't had one of these so I'm afraid I can't offer any tips, but I'm told it's painless, although as with the CT scan, having to lie still for so long can get uncomfortable.

## MEDICAL PROCEDURES AND PARAPHERNALIA

As far as hospital procedures are concerned, do ask your nurses before you have an operation what you are going to wake up with. If you know you will have any or all of the tubes and drains mentioned below, it can save you unnecessary alarm or confusion when you wake up. All suggestions are tried and tested by me!

### Catheter

This is used to empty your bladder automatically, and is usually inserted at the time of an operation and under anaesthetic. It may be put in later, but it doesn't hurt too much anyway, and it will usually be removed after a couple of days. For the first few days after the operation, the pain-killing drugs you will receive will ensure that you don't even feel the catheter. When you get more mobile, be careful not to drag on the tube coming out from your bladder, as it smarts. Most people are glad to get rid of their catheter by the time it has to be removed, but then you'll probably miss having it when you have to get out of bed to trail off to the loo. If you have any problem weeing for the first few times after the catheter is taken out, try sitting in (on?) a bidet of warm water to relax your muscles. If there isn't a bidet on the ward, take a bedpan into a warm bath, but of course that's more of a performance because you'll have to dry your legs off. But after the first couple of goes you shouldn't have any more problems anyway.

### Colostomy

When a person is having surgery for bowel cancer, the surgeon will try to resect (cut out) the part that is affected by tumour, and join up the two healthy ends. When this is not possible because the cancer is too near the rectum or there is not enough remaining bowel to join together once diseased bowel is removed, a colostomy will allow faeces to leave the body into a bag which you wear on your side. Sometimes a colostomy is temporary, sometimes permanent. There is a self-help organisation for people with colostomies, to help show that thousands of people have them and live with them with no problems (see p. 134).

## Drain

This is a tube coming out of the area of an operation, designed to suction out any blood or other fluid from the site. It can be a bit of a shock when you first see it with blood in it, but its purpose is to speed recovery and reduce the risk of infection, so try to see it as an aid rather than an irritation. Again, I never found drains to be any problem. They are usually removed after a few days and although the sensation is odd and can be briefly painful, it's all over in seconds. My only advice is – don't look!

## Intravenous drip

This just means the slow release of various fluids into your veins. Drips may be used to deliver saline solution into your body after an operation; they can also be used for pain-killers, blood and anti-coagulants. You may receive chemotherapy fully or partly by drip. I never found them any problem, but they may become a bit uncomfortable after several days, or if they are yanked by accident, so if you have one that is annoying you, mention it to the nurses because it can probably be made more comfortable. Once you are mobile, you can take your drip round with you on a tall stand. These behave in the same way as supermarket trollies in that they are quite incapable of moving in straight lines, but they're not very heavy and you'll soon get used to pushing yours around, probably with your catheter bag and drain bottle too!

## Naso-gastric tube

This can be used for feeding, but after an operation it is more likely to be used to suck out any gunge that is gathering in your stomach that would make you feel nauseated if it were left. It sounds horrible, but in fact you can't see it when you've got one in, so why should *you* worry! And it's not particularly uncomfortable although it does make talking a little difficult.

It's usually put in under anaesthetic, and when it's taken out, which doesn't hurt, it's done in seconds. I've even had one put in without anaesthetic and it really isn't such a big deal – as with so many of these things, the idea of it is worse than the reality.

### Stoma

This is an artificial opening to the outside of the body. It may be done from the trachea (windpipe), the larynx, or most commonly from the small or large bowel. If you need a stoma, specialist nurses will help you with getting used to it, caring for the opening and adjusting to it. If you need such a procedure, you will also find that there will be a self-help group available specially for people with your needs.

With all these gadgets, when it's time to remove them, try to get a nurse rather than a doctor to do it. They've had more practice, so they do it more quickly and with the minimum of discomfort.

## TREATMENT

### Chemotherapy

Chemotherapy at its most basic is controlled poison. Drugs known to be fatal to cancer cells will be directed at the area of tumour. The treatment may be used as a first line of attack, or as a secondary treatment designed to sweep the area around the site of an operation in the hope of catching any rogue cells that may be lurking there. Some chemotherapy drugs are more toxic than others, and your reaction to them will also depend on what area is being treated and your normal nausea susceptibility. So if you get very seasick, for example, or were very sick in pregnancy, you may unfortunately have a stronger reaction to the drugs. Cancer cells, once killed, cannot reproduce or mend themselves in the way that healthy cells can, so although some side-effects are inevitable, they are in the main short-lived, and any damage to normal cells can be repaired in time by the body.

The experience of chemotherapy, like the idea of cancer itself, seems to have an image in people's minds that I believe is exaggerated and causes needless fear. Like any treatment of illness, it can be unpleasant or even horrible, but you will almost certainly be able to be greatly helped by anti-nausea drugs which are becoming more and more effective. I also found that I could minimise the discomfort for myself by a few tricks of diet and relaxation.

The following description of the actual treatment may only apply in a broad sense to your own experience, but the side-effects I mention here and elsewhere (see Chapter 2) are an amalgam of many people's reactions, so would seem to be true for a great range of the drugs used.

Chemotherapy is delivered by drip, or by tablets, or by a combination of both, depending on your particular cancer and the target of treatment. The number of treatments and the timing will also vary and do not necessarily imply anything about your condition.

Your doctor should be able to tell you in advance whether you must expect to lose your hair or not. If you are likely to lose all your hair, wigs are available from the NHS – free if you are an in-patient, and for a nominal charge to out-patients. A variety of styles are available including punk, so do ask to see a catalogue. If you want something more elaborate in real hair, I know people who investigated the types available commercially before they began treatment. Two London department stores even agreed to put aside wigs for them without deposit in case they were needed. So it might be worth making your plans in advance while you're feeling stronger, so that you're ready if and when it happens (see also p. 57).

If, as in my case, the ends of your fingers go white and numb, you should mention it as it may need to be monitored. Although this is not a common reaction, if it is a problem for you, it is important not to allow yourself to get very chilled in winter. When this has happened to me, I have felt very ill, sometimes for a couple of days, and it can so easily be avoided.

I found it helped me to deal with the side-effects to:
~ Eat sparingly for a couple of days before each treatment,

and for about a week after and drink plenty, especially water. But don't skip meals altogether as an empty stomach is more prone to nausea. Glucose in skimmed milk goes down easily and gives an energy boost without bulk or puke-inducing fat. ~ Rest as much as possible, and try to lie down flat for at least an hour each day. I always felt more queasy if I was weary or if I tried to stay on my feet all day.

When I felt bad, I'd imagine the chemo drugs as the cavalry riding over the hill, or as the Star Wars fighters zooming in on the Death Star, bombarding the baddies with knockout blows and turning away victorious and triumphant. When all else failed, I'd pop off in my mind to my peaceful place in France, imagining myself as happy and rested (see Relaxation Techniques p. 100).

### Radiotherapy

Radiotherapy uses carefully directed high energy rays to destroy cancer cells. Normal cells which get in the way of the rays may also be damaged, but they can mend themselves whereas cancer cells can't. Radiotherapy may be used instead of surgery, especially where tumours are in particularly inaccessible or sensitive areas, such as the brain. It is more often used as a secondary treatment after surgery, as a sort of back-up to knock out any remaining cancer cells which the surgery didn't catch.

You may have to travel quite a distance to a radiotherapy centre, so that even though the treatment itself takes only a few minutes, a lot of the day may be swallowed up. If you need help, you can get ambulance transport but from what I saw the waiting can be very long and tedious, as the drivers have to wait for all the patients from different hospital departments to be ready to leave. Patients having treatment got a special car-parking pass at the hospital I attended, so it's worth asking if there are any concessions.

The dose of radiation is small and given over a period of weeks, so you don't need to worry about the possibility of radiation sickness, or that you are radioactive while you are having the most common form of radiotherapy treatment, which is given externally by a large machine. (If your doctor specifies internal radiotherapy, a radioactive source will need to be placed inside the body. This is done under anaesthetic and you may have to stay in hospital. You will be radioactive as long as the source is inside your body, and may have to be kept in isolation for a few days.)

The initial preparations can be rather intimidating, but the staff are usually well aware of people's feelings, so do ask if you need any further information or help.

An outline of the area is taken, and careful measurements recorded so that exactly the right spot is targeted. A blue dye is pinpricked under the skin so that the staff can 'line you up' each time you have treatment. If you need treatment to the head or face, you won't have to walk around with tattoos on your forehead. A special mould will be taken by applying a quick-setting cream to your skin, which is lifted off as soon as it is set. This serves both to mark precisely the treatment target, and to keep your head still while the machine is in action. Making the mould can be an unpleasant or claustro-phobic experience, but it only needs doing once.

You may need to have other marks on your body which must not be washed off until treatment is finished. If you have the tiny tattoos, you don't need to worry about washing as they are permanent – but don't worry about that either as nobody (not even your closest friends) will know they're there unless you tell them! You will probably be told of any general restrictions on bathing and cosmetics while you are having treatment, or given a leaflet with all the details.

While you are having radiotherapy, you will also be having regular blood tests. As with chemotherapy, the treatment can knock out your white cells, and the staff will need to keep a check on this so that if the level drops too low, they can alter your regime. But I've never met anyone to whom this did happen, although I do know people whose chemotherapy sessions were postponed because of low cell counts. You will also probably see a doctor at regular intervals (more long waits) to monitor how you're feeling. If as a result of seeing a doctor, a change to your treatment programme is suggested, don't assume that something is wrong, but use the opportunity to ask about the change and any other problems you are experiencing.

The things I found helpful as I went through radiotherapy are quite similar to my suggestions for chemotherapy. I'd always recommend Maxijul glucose in skimmed milk as a good way to boost your energy, especially if you can't face other food. About twenty minutes after drinking a couple of glasses of this concoction, you get a real rush of energy; it must be how Popeye feels when he swallows his spinach. The other advantage of Maxijul is that it doesn't taste sweet like other glucose preparations, so you can mix more of it into a drink. It's all a matter of personal taste, but I found the purpose-made drink supplements you can buy in chemists were far too sweet and frankly disgusting. I still use the glucose now when my gut is very irritated – and no, I don't have shares in the company! The only drawback is that you will probably have to order it from the chemist but it only takes a day or so. Another good one is Hi-Cal, which tastes okay when diluted with fizzy water, but it offers only calories, whereas the Maxijul milk will give you calories and protein, the two things you need most to start repairing yourself.

I know I keep going on about it, but I found it absolutely vital to get enough rest. Symptoms of nausea and lowness are made much worse if you're tired, and both the journey to hospital and the radiotherapy itself are undeniably wearing. I always found that if I went shopping, or walked about too much, I would be exhausted out of all proportion to the effort involved in what I'd been doing – and I would take longer to feel better as well. It is so tempting when you are starting to recover after surgery to want to get back into circulation, but I certainly found that if I didn't pace myself I'd really regret it. As a rule of thumb, I reckon it took me three times as long as I'd spent doing whatever it was I shouldn't have been doing to recover from the strain of doing it! Of course it's a balancing act between what is best for your morale and what is best for your recovering body. The first time I managed to walk the half mile to collect my children from school I felt a great wave of triumph – but when I got home again (by car) I could have cried with exhaustion. But you will quickly learn what you can manage.

## Physiotherapy

Your nurses will probably get you up and out of bed as soon as possible after your operation. They're not being hearty or cruel; it's vital that you start revving up your circulation to avoid the risk of blood clots. You may find that you're wearing tight white stockings when you wake up from your operation as well – these are to help prevent clots forming in the legs. After a few days, if you're progressing normally, you will probably have a visit from the physiotherapist, who will suggest some exercises suitable for whatever operation you've had, and will encourage you to walk up and down for short distances, and perhaps up some stairs. If you have to do this several times a day, it can obviously be boring, but it's really important and will also make you feel better more quickly, because any remaining drug you may have had will get whizzed round your system and out the other end at a faster rate. I used to pretend I was horse-racing, and do a Peter O'Sullevan-type commentary to keep myself shuffling along. Try to add a few more steps each day so that you can see the improvement. Or walk with your Walkman!

Even if you can't get up for a while, you can do exercises in bed which will both make you feel better and give you the satisfaction of helping yourself rather than being a passive patient. Even pointing your toes, then pulling them back as far as you can, will speed up the all-important circulation.

## DRUGS FOR PAIN

Through all the treatment I had, I was never in any real pain. I hope that can reassure people, because a vast range of drugs can be prescribed for pain, and there is no reason to suffer in silence. There may, however, be drugs that you feel are too strong for you, or make you nauseated, so don't be afraid to ask for a change of prescription. For example, I found that one particular pain-killer made me vomit – not recommended after major surgery – and another made me feel unpleasantly dizzy. But there were others that did the job splendidly with no adverse affects at all.

A doctor will need to agree the change and sign for the new drugs, so don't wait until the pain is unbearable. And don't wait until the shift is changing when all the staff are making reports and nowhere to be seen. Don't refuse sleeping tablets or pain-killers if you don't think you need them that minute – make sure they will be easily available later if you change your mind.

You will probably find that after your operation you will have been 'written up' for pain-killers by the surgeon, which will probably be given by injection, and it's not likely that you will be asked whether you want them or not! But these doses will make you sleepy so if you think you can manage without them, do discuss it with your nurses. Personally I was only too happy to take whatever was going. (I want to mention again that while still coming round from the anaesthetic, I and other patients I know cried and moaned a lot about how much pain we were in and how terrible it all was – which was awful for our partners to listen to and of which we have no memory whatsoever! It might be worth mentioning to whoever will be holding *your* hand.)

You may well be amazed, as I always was, at the rate your body can mend, and after only a few days the pain-killing drugs can be stopped if you wish. But don't be a hero; it won't help you get better any quicker – in fact, pain is very wearing and bad for morale.


## DRUGS FOR NAUSEA

During chemotherapy you are likely to be given drugs to help minimise the nausea which is the most obvious side-effect of the cytotoxic (cancer-killing) drugs. Again there are choices available, so if one doesn't work for you, mention it at the next treatment session and ask for something else. New drugs are coming out all the time so there isn't any point in my giving you specific names, but I certainly had quite a cocktail for each session, so mixing these anti-nausea drugs together can't be a problem. You can also help the drugs to be more effective by eating sparingly before the treatment, and drinking twice as much as normal after it. And, for the millionth and last time, you will feel worse if you let yourself get too tired!

# 15

# Getting Help

I was very lucky in having someone who was always there for me, but however much support you have from those you love the best, there are going to be problems and fears that you can't talk to them about. To speak such thoughts aloud gives them a life of their own, and while I do believe you definitely should talk about your feelings, I also feel that some things cause more hurt if they're expressed to people who know you, and end up having longer-lasting effects than if you can find another release for them.

## HOSPICES

In this area I was greatly helped by the local hospice care team. Not only do they have experience of dealing with cancer patients and understanding of the problems facing them, but they have the added strength of being blessedly uninvolved. You can tell them of your fears of death and pain. You can talk about your worries about your partner being left alone, or of your children being scarred by early bereavement. You can express your feelings of bitterness and anger about the people who've let you down; you can tell them about the depths of your self-pity or the terror that descends when you're lying in bed. You can say whatever the hell you want to them – and they'll listen, they'll know what you're talking about, they won't think you're a terrible person or weak or selfish, and you won't be causing them pain or embarrassment. To me their visits seemed tremendously productive, as if my mind had been spring-cleaned, leaving me refreshed and reassured to plod on again. If you feel the service might be of use to you, your GP will refer you (in some areas the service may be provided by Macmillan nurses). Perhaps I should add that hospice care is not restricted to terminally ill patients; it can embrace anyone with a serious illness.

## SUPPORT ORGANISATIONS

Apart from the help offered by hospices, there are a number of independent organisations which offer information and counselling services. In the main, hospitals do not have the time or the staff to offer much in the way of counselling. It's basically a matter of lack of resources. Their priorities need to be directed to the practical business of keeping people alive. It's always worth asking what's available, but if you already have to travel some distance to the hospital, counselling sessions, even if they are available, may prove to be more exhausting than they're worth.

I got in touch with BACUP and CancerLink, but they could only offer meetings that were taking place a long way from my home, and in the evenings when I would already be in bed. I'm not trying to knock the support that these groups offer, but they are run voluntarily with little or no funding and simply can't meet individual needs on the spot. That's why I would suggest getting in touch with the support organisations before you even go into hospital, because you won't feel up to persevering when you come out.

Below you will find a list of the principal support organisations with details of what they offer.

**The British Association of Cancer United Patients (BACUP)**
3 Bath Place, Rivington Street, London EC2A 3JR
tel: 071-613 2121 (London)
Freephone 0800 181199 (outside London) for their information linkline.
BACUP helps patients and their families cope with cancer. Trained nurses offer practical advice and emotional support

by telephone or letter. BACUP produces a range of free publications and a newsletter. One-to-one counselling is available in Greater London (tel: 071-696 9000), and BACUP can also put you in touch with local groups.

**Breast Care and Mastectomy Association of Great Britain (BCMA)**
15–19 Britten Street, London SW3 3TZ
tel: 071-867 8275; for Helpline tel: 071-867 1103
Volunteers who themselves have experience of breast cancer offer emotional support nationwide. Practical advice and information is available from qualified staff.

**British Colostomy Association**
15 Station Road, Reading, Berkshire RG1 1LG
tel: 0734 391537
Personal and experienced advice and support for people learning to deal with a colostomy. Local contacts are available, and hospital or home visits can be arranged.

**Cancer Care Society (CARE)**
21 Zetland Road, Redland, Bristol BS6 7AH
tel: 0272 427419
An organisation of cancer patients formed into self-help groups. Branches and contacts throughout the country offer personal counselling information and advice as well as social functions. A telephone link service puts cancer patients in touch with one another.

**CancerLink**
17 Britannia Street, London WC1X 9JN
tel: 071-833 2451
Information and support by telephone and letter on all types of cancer and associated problems. CancerLink also has a network of hundreds of self-help groups throughout Britain. Free publications available.

## Cancer Relief Macmillan Fund
Anchor House, 15–19 Britten Street, London SW3 3TZ
tel: 071-351 7811
Skilled care and support for cancer patients and their families. Best known for the Macmillan nurses home service; also in-patient and day-care centres. Some grants available: apply through GP for nursing services; via your hospital or social services for other grants.

## Hodgkin's Disease Association
PO Box 275, Haddenham, Aylesbury, Bucks HP17 8JJ
tel: 0844 291500
Information and emotional support for lymphoma patients and their families. Booklets and video available. There is a nationwide network of experienced helpers.

## Hospice Information Service
St Christopher's Hospice, 51 Lawrie Park Road, London SE26 6DZ
tel: 081-778 9252
Directory of hospice services, including home-care teams and hospital support teams. These are the people who helped me so much when I had trouble adjusting to the threat of further recurrence.

## Hysterectomy Support Network
3 Lynne Close, Green Street Green, Orpington, Kent BR6 6BS
tel: 081-856 3881
(11 a.m. to 5 p.m. Mon, Wed, Fri)
Refers women who have had or are about to have the operation, and/or their family and partners, to women in their area who have themselves undergone a hysterectomy, for support and advice.

**Institute for Complementary Medicine**
PO Box 194, London SE16 1QZ
tel: 071-237 5165
Register of practitioners of homeopathy, osteopathy etc. Send SAE for information, stating what area of treatment you're interested in.

**Institute of Family Therapy**
43 New Cavendish Street, London W1M 7RG
tel: 071-935 1651
Counselling for families with members who are seriously ill, or those who are recently bereaved. The whole family is involved in treatment. The service is free, funded by voluntary donations.

**Leukaemia Care Society**
14 Kingfisher Court, Venny Bridge, Pinhoe, Exeter, Devon EX4 8JN
tel: 0392 64848
Friendship and support via a network of area secretaries for people with leukaemia and associated blood disorders.

**Malcolm Sargent Cancer Fund for Children**
14 Abingdon Road, London W8 6AF
tel: 071-937 4548
Grants for parents of children with cancer (up to age twenty-one) to help pay for equipment, travel, heating etc. Apply through hospital social worker.

**Marie Curie Cancer Care**
28 Belgrave Square, London SW1X 8QG
tel: 071-235 3325
Nursing care is available in eleven homes around the UK. Day and night nursing can be provided in patient's home through the Marie Curie Community Nursing Service (via your local health authority).

# 16

# Back To The Future

At the time of writing this book, my treatment has been finished for eighteen months, and all looks well. I don't think I could say that my emotional recovery has achieved the same level as my physical improvement but for most of the time, life is ordinary, quiet and happy.

I still take great pleasure in simple things that have returned to my daily routine. I love being able to take my children to school, a half-mile walk each way that was impossible for so long. I love being able to go to the supermarket and do my own shopping. I'm no longer flattened by a trip to the office, and I revel in the ability to do physical work, like shifting furniture or wrestling with duvet covers. I'm delighted to be able to stay up all day without sleeping in the afternoon.

How long a trip round Sainsbury's will continue to seem like a minor miracle is of course debatable; perhaps I will only be truly recovered when I take as many things for granted as I did before! But for the time being I try to keep on taking each day as it comes, and I know I make more time for the pleasures it offers. So many things seem like a bonus. Watching my kids running around on a beach, seeing the changes of the seasons in our garden, walking our new puppy – how's that for optimism? I'm still around to do it, and I'm well enough to enjoy it.

Minor irritations don't bother me much either: they just don't seem that important. I feel that I live at a much calmer pace and I make a conscious effort to get more out of life. Once you've realised how fragile a thing your life can be, rushing about to score points at work, or wondering when you'll be able to afford to replace the sofa that's about to collapse thanks to junior gymnastics really don't come very high on the list of priorities.

I still have bowel problems, and have to restrict my diet quite a lot, so I know that I'm reminded more often than most about what's happened. (I must stress once again that these problems are not an inevitable, or even a common, result of bowel surgery. I know two men, one in his late sixties, who were both back on steak and chips after three months!) But as time goes on, I've become familiar with all my local facilities. It may be hard to believe, as incontinence is not the most dignified of problems, but it really doesn't bother me any more except that I still won't travel on the Tube (because I can't get off if I need to) and I do have to plan my days, but you can get used to anything given long enough. And you wouldn't believe how good it's possible to feel on Boxing Day and New Year's Day if you know you can't overdo the eating and drinking.

I still wonder about every ache and pain, though not with the panic of a year ago. Usually I can control the fear far better now, though I still get up some nights and come downstairs to read trashy novels (I never did get used to all-night TV) though my concentration is so much better that I can actually read books with real plots.

The more time that passes, the fewer bad days there are, and I've spoken to people who finished treatment many years ago who've told me they truly hardly ever think about it any more. That seems hard to believe at the moment, but when I remind myself how far I've come, then I have more confidence that one day I too will put it all behind me.

The one impossibility at the moment is for it all to be finally over. There isn't a day when some part of the past three years doesn't come back to me. Sometimes this impossibility of just forgetting makes me mad. I want to look at my children and not wonder if I'll be around to see them graduate, or marry, or if I'll make it to being a grandmother. I want to feel able to make plans with my husband for our future and not feel that we're either kidding ourselves or somehow tempting fate.

At the moment, whatever I said about the puppy, I can't even bring myself to book my next dental appointment for six months' time. But even if I can't yet take the future for granted, I know that most of the time I am at peace, which is good enough.

I'm afraid I still can't see that my cancer experience taught me anything I particularly wanted to know, or proved creative in any way. I have been lucky; I am grateful to have survived, but I know what these years have cost us and the memories are bitter. My world has shrunk to each day, and to my husband and the children, and I am the poorer for that hardening of my heart.

So there are still negative feelings that have to be fought against, because to allow them free run would mean that cancer takes even more of my life away from me, and I will not allow that. I had a letter from one cancer patient who said she thought we would always carry with us the wounds of our cancer experience, what she called our 'emotional limp'. I think she was probably right up to a point, but I intend to have the kind of limp that only plays me up when the weather is very bad indeed!

The year this book comes out I will celebrate my fortieth birthday as no fortieth has ever been celebrated before. There were so many moments when to get there at all seemed impossible to imagine, and I will welcome it with open arms – middle age has never seemed so precious. Fifty would be even better, and I promise I'll be the happiest seventy-year-old you'll ever meet.

Finally my favourite quote of all, which is from a medieval woman called Dame Julian, who lived in an anchorite's cell in Norwich and had the most wonderfully comforting thoughts. I always imagine her as some apple-cheeked, vast-bosomed lady smelling of warm baking and flowery scent, and her sayings as a sort of enveloping hug which makes you feel totally safe. These particular words seemed to me to sum up everything that happened, and give me a great sense of calm. I hope they can do the same for you.

> *He did not say thou shouldst not be troubled, travailed, distressed. He did say thou shalt not be overcome.*